English in Action
Workbook

3

Barbara H. Foley

Elizabeth R. Neblett

HEINLE
CENGAGE Learning™

Australia • Brazil • Japan • Korea • Mexico • Singapore • Spain • United Kingdom • United States

HEINLE
CENGAGE Learning

English in Action 3, Workbook
Barbara H. Foley, Elizabeth R. Neblett

Publisher, Adult and Academic ESL:
James W. Brown

Senior Acquisitions Editor: Sherrise Roehr

Developmental Editor: Sarah Barnicle

Assistant Editor: Audra Longert

Senior Marketing Manager, Adult ESL:
Donna Lee Kennedy

Director, Global ESL Training & Development:
Evelyn Nelson

Senior Production Editor: Maryellen Killeen

Senior Frontlist Buyer: Mary Beth Hennebury

Project Manager: Tünde A. Dewey

Compositor: Pre-Press Co., Inc.

Production Services: Pre-Press Company, Inc.

Text Printer/Binder: West Group

Text Designer: Sue Gerald

Cover Designer: Gina Petti/Rotunda Design
House

Photo Researcher: Jill Engerbretson

Photography Manager: Sheri Blaney

Cover Art: Zita Asbaghi/Unit Opener Art:
Zita Asbaghi

Illustrators: Scott MacNeill; Ray Medici
Glen Giron, Roger Acaya, Ibarra
Cristostomo, Leo Cultura of Raketshop
Design Studio, Philippines

Library of Congress Control Number: 2004117882

ISBN-13: 978-0-8384-5199-1
ISBN-10: 0-8384-5199-3

Heinle
25 Thomson Place
Boston, Massachusetts 02210
USA

Cengage Learning is a leading provider of customized learning solutions with office locations around the globe, including Singapore, the United Kingdom, Australia, Mexico, Brazil, and Japan. Locate your local office at:
international.cengage.com/region

Cengage Learning products are represented in Canada by Nelson Education, Ltd.

Visit Heinle online at **elt.heinle.com**

Visit our corporate website at **cengage.com**

Printed in the United States of America
6 7 11 10 09 08

Contents

1 The First Week

☀ Practicing on Your Own

1. Complete each story with the correct verb from the box.

am studying	know	studied	am going to enroll
use	meet	got	✓ is

1. Hi. My name _____ **is** _____ Luisa. I _____ ESL in an intensive program. My classes _____ five days a week from 9:00 A.M. to 2:00 P.M. I already _____ some English because I _____ English in my country for four years. Also, I just _____ a job in a jewelry store, so I _____ English at work. Next year, I _____ in regular college classes.

didn't study	came	speak	attend	is	is

2. Good afternoon. My name _____ Boris. I _____ to the United States two years ago with my son and daughter-in-law. I _____ English in my country, so I _____ adult school two nights a week. All my friends _____ Russian, so it _____ difficult for me to practice English.

works	are living	attends	am studying
is	get	am	talk

3. Hello. My name _____ Mia. I _____ from Taiwan. My husband _____ for a large international company. Right now, we _____ in the United States. I _____ English at a small private school. My daughter _____ public school. I sometimes _____ together with other mothers and we _____ about our children.

2. Complete this conversation with the questions from the box.

> Where do you live?
> Do you have any children?
> ✓ What country are you from?
> What kind of music do you like?
> How long have you been here?
> Is your family here?

A: What country are you from? _____

B: I'm from Vietnam.

A: _____

B: I live in Houston, Texas.

A: _____

B: Yes, my whole family is here.

A: _____

B: I've been here for eight years.

A: _____

B: No, I don't have any children. I'm not married.

A: _____

B: I like country music.

3. Answer these questions about yourself.

1. What country are you from?

   _____

2. Where do you live?

   _____

3. How long have you been in the United States?

   _____

4. Where do you go to school?

   _____

5. How many days a week do you study English?

   _____

6. Are you married or single? Do you have any children?

   _____

7. What are your interests?

   _____

4. Complete these sentences about the student center. Write one of the expressions from the box and *is* or *are*. Several answers are possible.

None of the students
One of the students
A couple of the students
A few of the students

Some of the students
Many of the students
Most of the students
All of the students

1. <u>Many of the students are</u> _____ sitting.

2. _____ playing cards.

3. _____ relaxing.

4. _____ ordering pizza.

5. _____ studying together.

6. _____ playing chess.

7. _____ ordering a cup of coffee.

8. _____ using a computer.

9. _____ wearing comfortable clothes.

10. _____ talking on a cell phone.

5. Answer these questions about the student center on page 4.

Yes, there is. No, there isn't.	Yes, there are. No, there aren't.	Yes, they are. No, they aren't.	Yes, it is. No, it isn't.	Yes, he is. No, he isn't.

1. Are there many students in the student center? _____ Yes, there are. _____
2. Are some students playing chess? _____
3. Is Jamal smiling? _____
4. Are some students studying? _____
5. Is one student ordering coffee? _____
6. Are some students watching TV? _____
7. Is Bill tired? _____
8. Is he interested in the TV program? _____
9. Is one student ordering pizza? _____
10. Are there some video games in the center? _____
11. Is the student center busy? _____
12. Is there a soda machine in the student center? _____
13. Are there any children in the student center? _____
14. Is the student center large? _____

6. Write the third person singular of the verbs in the box. Then, use the correct form of the verb in the sentences.

meet _____ meets _____	give _____
study _____	live _____
take _____	speak _____
have _____	

1. Jamal _____ has _____ English class three days a week.
2. His class _____ for three hours.
3. Jamal also _____ math and science.
4. His teachers _____ a lot of homework.
5. He _____ five hours a day.
6. Jamal _____ in a dormitory.
7. Many students _____ in his dorm.
8. Most of the students _____ English.

7. Listen and complete this school diagram.

security desk	men's room	copy machine	student lounge
elevators	women's room	counselor's office	ATM machine
stairs	bookstore	nurse's office	vending machines

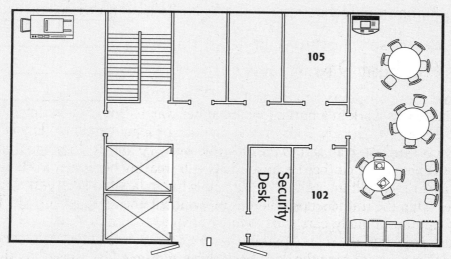

8. Listen and copy only the true sentences about your school.

1. _____

2. _____

3. _____

4. _____

5. _____

6. _____

7. _____

9. Listen and circle the letter of the correct response.

1. a. It's in room 416.   b. I'm in my office from 1:00 to 2:00.
2. a. 12 Broad Street.   b. orange@ccc.edu
3. a. The library is on the first floor.   b. Show your ID at the library desk.
4. a. Yes, it's in room 318.   b. All students can use the labs.
5. a. Please give me your number.   b. No. Turn off your cell phones before class.
6. a. Do pages 34 and 35.   b. On Monday.

7.	**a.** You need to buy two books.	**b.**	It's on the first floor.
8.	**a.** It's open from 9:00 to 9:00.	**b.**	You need a library card.
9.	**a.** Yes, but we have only one.	**b.**	No, I didn't take a vacation.
10.	**a.** Please study for the test.	**b.**	It's next Wednesday.
11.	**a.** We finish on June 10.	**b.**	You are expected to attend every class.
12.	**a.** Yes, there is a final exam.	**b.**	Our first exam is tomorrow.
13.	**a.** This is intermediate ESL.	**b.**	There are five levels.
14.	**a.** I hope you feel better.	**b.**	Talk to me when you return.

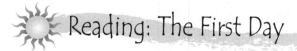

Reading: The First Day

Raisa leaves work in a hurry, looking at her watch. She usually finishes work at 5:00, but it is 6:00 already. Today is the first day of school and her class begins at 7:00. The school is all the way across the city. She won't be able to go home first. Raisa wants to change her clothes because she is still wearing her green work uniform. There isn't time for dinner either, so she pulls into a fast-food drive-up window. A few minutes later, the traffic stops. There is an accident ahead. Raisa just sits for the next twenty minutes. Finally, cars start to move again.

Raisa pulls into the school parking lot at 6:55 and walks quickly to her classroom. The teacher is just closing the door. She smiles and says, "Hi, Raisa." As she walks to the back, looking for a seat, several other students say, "Hi, Raisa." Raisa smiles as she realizes, "Of course they know my name! I'm still wearing my name tag."

Class starts and the students introduce themselves. Three other students are from her country and many students have been in the United States a long time, too. Some of the other students were stuck in the same traffic jam. After a while, Raisa relaxes. The teacher is friendly and the class is interesting. Raisa knows it isn't always going to be easy to get to class, but she is glad that she started English classes today.

Answer these questions.

1. Is Raisa's workplace close to her school?   _____ No, it isn't. _____

2. Did Raisa work overtime today?   _____

3. Why can't she change her clothes?   _____

4. Where does Raisa eat her dinner?   _____

5. Why is the traffic stopped?   _____

6. Is Raisa late for class?   _____

7. How do the students know her name?   _____

8. Is Raisa new to the United States?   _____

2 The Average American

Practicing on Your Own

I work.	He works.
You work.	She works.
We work.	It works.
They work.	

1. Circle the correct answer.

1. Most Americans **drive** / **drives** to work.

2. The average American **drive** / **drives** to work alone.

I don't work.	He doesn't work.
You don't work.	She doesn't work.
We don't work.	It doesn't work.
They don't work.	

3. The average American **don't walk** / **doesn't walk** to work.

4. Many Americans **don't take** / **doesn't take** public transportation to work.

5. Americans **like** / **likes** to spend the evening watching TV or videos.

6. Sometimes American families **eat** / **eats** dinner out.

7. Most American families **have** / **has** barbecues on the Fourth of July.

8. The average American **eat** / **eats** hamburgers, hot dogs, or chicken on the Fourth of July.

9. Most Fourth of July fireworks **come** / **comes** from China.

2. Complete the sentences. Write the correct form of the verb in parentheses. Some of the verbs are negative.

1. The average American _____lives_____ (live) in a house.

2. In the Midwest, most Americans _____don't live_____ (live—negative) in apartments.

3. The average American _____ (move) many times.

4. Most Americans _____ (move) into larger homes.

5. Most Americans _____ (live—negative) in apartments.

6. The average American _____ (move—negative) for health reasons.

7. I _____ (want) to move to a different climate.

8. I _____ (live) in a two-family house.

9. I _____ (plan) to move this year.

3. Read the graphs and complete the sentences. Use the simple present tense of the verbs in parentheses. Some of the verbs are negative.

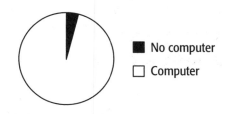

No computer
Computer

Do you have a computer? (have)

1. The average American __has__ a computer.

2. Five percent of Americans _____ computers at home.

3. I _____ a computer at home.

4. My classroom _____ computers for the students to use.

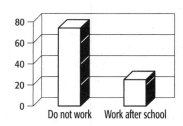

Do not work   Work after school

Do high school students work? (work)

1. Most high school students _____ part-time after school.

2. Twenty-six percent of high school students _____ part-time after school.

3. I _____ part-time.

4. High school students in my country _____ part-time.

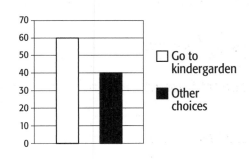

Go to kindergarden
Other choices

Do all children go to kindergarten? (go)

1. Most children _____ to kindergarten.

2. The average child _____ to kindergarten.

3. Some children _____ to kindergarten; their parents make other choices for them.

4. Most children in my country _____ to kindergarten.

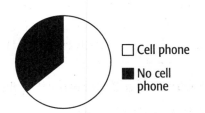

Cell phone
No cell phone

Do you own a cell phone? (own)

1. The average American _____ a cell phone.

2. Most Americans _____ cell phones.

3. I _____ a cell phone.

4. The members of my family _____ cell phones.

4. *Yes/No questions.* Read and answer the questions.

1. Do you live in an apartment? _____ Yes, I do. _____

2. Do you speak English every day? _____

3. Do you speak your native language at work? _____

4. Do you watch the news every day? _____

5. Do you enjoy movies? _____

6. Does your teacher speak your native language? _____

7. Does your teacher give homework every day? _____

8. Does it rain a lot in your city? _____

9. Does it take a long time to learn English? _____

5. *How often . . . ?* Read and answer the questions using a time expression or an adverb of frequency.

every morning	once a week
every day	twice a month
every night	three times a year

I am **always** on time.	I **always** arrive on time.
He is **usually** on time.	He **usually** arrives on time.
You are **often** on time.	You **often** arrive on time.
I am **sometimes** late.	I **sometimes** arrive late.
She is **seldom** late.	She **seldom** arrives late.
They are **never** on time.	They **never** arrive on time.

1. How often are you late for English class?

   _____

2. How often do you take public transportation?

   _____

3. How often are you homesick for your country?

   _____

4. How often does your teacher give tests?

   _____

5. How often does your class meet?

   _____

6. How often is your teacher absent?

   _____

7. How often do students in your class listen to tapes or CDs in class?

   _____

8. How often do you and your family rent movies?

   _____

6. The average American woman. Read the information about the average American woman.

The lifestyle of the average American woman	Statistics
1. Has a high school diploma	84%
2. Has a college degree	25%
3. Has a full-time job	50%
4. Full-time salary	$29,215
5. Votes in major elections	61%
6. Age at her first marriage	25.1 years old
7. Is a working mother with infant children	55%

Source: U.S. Census

Complete the sentences with the information from the chart. Use the correct present tense form of the verbs in parentheses. Some of the sentences are negative.

1. Most American women _____have_____ (have) high school diplomas.

2. The average American woman _____ (have) a college degree.

3. The average salary for women _____ (be) $29,215.

4. Most American women _____ (earn) less than $30,000 a year.

5. Half of the women in the United States _____ (work) full-time.

6. The average American woman _____ (vote) in major elections.

7. The average American woman _____ (get) married at 25.1 years of age.

8. Many women with infant children _____ (work) outside the home.

7. Edit. There are six present tense verb mistakes in the paragraph. Find and correct five more mistakes.

Every Thursday after work, Angela, Jackie, and Sara ~~goes~~ **go** out to dinner. Every week, the women spends one evening without their husbands or children. They don't talks about problems. They just enjoy an evening out, have a nice dinner, and goes to a movie. Each week a different person choose the restaurant and the movie. After the movie at 10:00 or 10:30, the women makes plans for the next week.

Listening

8. Listen to David, a teenager, talk about his eating habits. Then, answer the questions.

1. Does David eat breakfast every day? _____ No, he doesn't.

2. Does he sometimes eat fruit at breakfast? _____

3. Does David eat lunch every day? _____

4. Does David take his lunch to school or buy lunch? _____

5. Do David and his classmates eat out sometimes? _____

6. How often do David and his family eat dinner together? _____

7. How often do David and his family eat out? _____

8. What does David's family like to eat when they go out? _____

9. Listen and write the sentences.

> **carpool:** When a group of people takes turns driving the group to work, they are carpooling.
> **commute:** to travel back and forth regularly, usually to a job

1. Teenage boys often like to eat out. _____

2. _____

3. _____

4. _____

5. _____

6. _____

7. _____

8. _____

Reading: Home Schooling

Most American children attend public or private schools with other children in a traditional setting. The traditional school has classrooms, a cafeteria, a gym, and other facilities. Today, a growing number of children do not attend traditional schools; they stay at home and participate in home schooling.

Who chooses home schooling? The typical family consists of two parents and children, with only one working parent, usually the father. The parents are usually well educated and can teach their children what they need to know.

There are many reasons why parents choose home schooling for their children. First, some parents think that they can give their children a better education than the local school can. Second, the parents do not like the school curriculum or what the school teaches their children. A third reason is that the parents think that the school's lessons are too easy for their children. Another reason is because of the strong religious beliefs of the family.

The Internet is making home schooling a little easier for parents. Some states, including Florida and Illinois, offer courses for home-schooled students. Home-schooled students can join "classes" with other home schoolers through discussion lists, instant messaging, and video lectures.

Public schools can help home-schooled students. They allow the home-schooled students to participate in after-school activities such as sports and chorus. Therefore, the students do not miss the social part of school—making friends, talking to classmates, and learning to work with different people.

Read each statement. Circle T for _True_ or F for _False_.

1. Most American children attend traditional schools.   (T)   F

2. Home-schooled students eat in school cafeterias.   T   (F)

3. A home-schooled child usually has two working parents.   T   (F)

4. Parents choose home-schooling because it is cheaper.   T   (F)

5. Parents want to choose what their children learn.   (T)   F

6. Some parents think the regular school lessons are too difficult.   T   (F)

7. All parents with strong religious beliefs prefer traditional school.   T   (F)

8. Home schooling is easier because of the Internet.   (T)   F

9. Home-schooled students have to play sports at home.   T   (F)

What's your opinion? What do you think about home schooling? Write your opinion.

_____

_____

_____

3 Pets

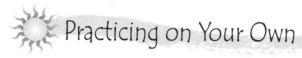
1. Look at the information under each set of pictures. Answer the questions about the pets and their owners.

Ana

Doberman—Max

+ great watchdog
− eats a lot

Tony

Cat—Midnight

+ easy to care for
− new girlfriend is allergic to cats

Marcus

Poodle—Molly

+ affectionate
− barks a lot

1. Does Ana have a Doberman? _____ **Yes, she does.** _____
2. Is Max a large dog? _____
3. Is he a good watchdog? _____
4. Does Ana feel safe at home alone? _____
5. Does Max eat a lot? _____
6. Does Tony have a dog? _____
7. Does he like cats? _____
8. Is Midnight black? _____
9. Is Midnight easy to care for? _____
10. Is Tony's new girlfriend allergic to cats? _____
11. Does Marcus have a poodle? _____
12. Is Molly affectionate? _____
13. Does Molly bark a lot? _____
14. Do you like cats? _____
15. Do you have a pet? _____

2. Complete these *Yes/No* questions about your class with *Do, Does, Is,* or *Are*. Then, answer the questions.

1. ___Do___ you attend school five days a week? _____
2. _____ your school in a large city? _____
3. _____ you talkative in class? _____
4. _____ your teacher married? _____
5. _____ your teacher give a lot of homework? _____
6. _____ you always do your homework? _____
7. _____ your class meet in the morning? _____
8. _____ you drive to school? _____
9. _____ you sometimes late for class? _____
10. _____ this exercise difficult? _____
11. _____ your school have a bookstore? _____
12. _____ you bring your dictionary to class? _____

3. Complete these questions with a question phrase from the box.

How large	What kind of	What	How
How often	Are	When	Where
How many	How much		

1. ___What kind of___ pet do you have?   Fish.
2. _____ fish do you have?   About 50.
3. _____ is your aquarium?   One hundred gallons.
4. _____ is your aquarium?   In my living room.
5. _____ do you feed them?   In the morning.
6. _____ do you feed them?   Fish food.
7. _____ do you clean the aquarium?   Once a month.
8. _____ do fish cost?   Between $3 and $50 each.
9. _____ fish do you have?   Tropical fish.
10. _____ do you buy them?   At a pet store.
11. _____ do you learn about fish?   From reading about them.
12. _____ your fish friendly?   Of course they are!

4. Laura is a veterinarian. Put the words in the correct order to write questions.

1. Laura / Where / work / does
   <u>**Where does Laura work?**</u>
   She works at an animal hospital in the Midwest.

2. she / hours a day / How / does / many / work
   _____
   She works ten hours a day.

3. treat / kind of / does / What / animals / she
   _____
   She treats all kinds of animals.

4. does / earn / much / she / How
   _____
   She earns $80,000 a year.

5. Complete these questions about Laura's schedule.

6:00	Wake up.
6:30	Walk Dot and Spot in the park.
7:30	Eat breakfast.
8:00 – 12:00	Office hours. See patients.
12:00 – 12:30	Eat lunch.
12:30 – 2:00	Do paperwork.
2:00 – 6:00	Visit patients on farms.
7:00	Eat dinner.
8:00	Watch TV, read.

1. What time ____**does**____ Laura ____**wake up**____?   At 6:00.

2. How many dogs _____ she _____?   Two.

3. Where _____ she _____ her dogs?   In the park.

4. _____ Laura _____ breakfast?   Yes, she does.

5. When _____ her office hours?   From 8:00 to 12:00.

6. _____ she _____ an hour for lunch?   No, she doesn't.

7. When _____ she _____ paperwork?   From 12:30 to 2:00.

8. Where _____ she _____ patients in the afternoon?   On farms.

9. What _____ she _____ at night?   She watches TV and reads.

6. Read about this pet cockatiel. Then, write the questions about the information.

Cockatiels

I have a pet cockatiel named Harry. Harry is gray with a yellow head. He's 12 inches long. He's very friendly. He likes me to pick him up and pet him. He sits on my shoulder when I read or watch TV. He can speak and knows about 100 words.

I bought Harry about two years ago when he was six weeks old. I bought a male cockatiel because male birds are talkers. Female cockatiels are very quiet and often do not learn to speak. Harry is easy to take care of. He lives in a large cage in my living room. He eats bird seed and chopped vegetables, and his favorite treat is peas. I put a fresh cup of water in his cage each morning.

Harry is by himself most of the day, so I keep the TV on to keep him company. When I come home, he is ready to talk and play. I take him out of his cage and pet him and talk to him. If I want to teach him a new word or phrase, I repeat it over and over. After a few days or a few weeks, he starts to say it. Cockatiels have a long life expectancy, often 25 years or more. Harry and I are going to be companions for a long time.

1. What kind of pet _does she have_____?

2. What color _____?

3. Can _____?

4. How many words _____?

5. How old _____?

6. Are _____?

7. Is _____?

8. Where _____?

9. What _____?

10. Why _____?

11. When _____?

12. How long _____?

Listening

7. Listen and circle the correct answers.

1. **a.** He's a German shepherd.   **b.** He's very big.
2. **a.** His name is Stormy.   **b.** My name is Martin.
3. **a.** He was $400.   **b.** He's 80 pounds.
4. **a.** Yes, he is.   **b.** Yes, he does.
5. **a.** Yes, I have two children.   **b.** Yes, he's very good with children.
6. **a.** Yes, he is.   **b.** Yes, he stays in the house.
7. **a.** He's brown.   **b.** He's four.
8. **a.** My son does.   **b.** My son is.
9. **a.** Yes, we do.   **b.** Yes, we are.
10. **a.** No, he isn't.   **b.** No, he doesn't.

8. Lauri is a dog walker. Read the answers. Then, listen and write the question next to the correct answer.

1. _____   I'm a dog walker.
2. _____   Two or three dogs.
3. _____   In the park.
4. _____   About 20.
5. _____   Once a day.
6. _____   Yes, I'm very tired.
7. How long do you walk the dogs? _____   About 30 minutes.
8. _____   I charge $10 per walk.

9. Listen to the information about Chihuahuas. Then, circle T for True or F or False.

1. Chihuahuas are noisy dogs.   (T)   F
2. Chihuahuas are affectionate dogs.   T   F
3. A Chihuahua is a good dog for a large family.   T   F
4. Chihuahuas like cold weather.   T   F

 Reading: Pet Therapy

In pet therapy programs, pet owners bring their dogs, cats, or other small animals to visit patients in hospitals, nursing homes, or other programs for the sick or elderly. In most programs, volunteers bring their pets twice a month. Patients hold the animals, pet them, and talk to them. Pets also make it easier for patients to talk to other people. They often talk about memories of pets they miss or used to own.

Pet visits help patients feel better, both **physically** and **emotionally**. Studies show that pets can lower blood pressure and **reduce** stress. Animals can help a patient forget about pain or loneliness. Patients welcome a visitor who offers love and affection, paying little attention to age or illness. In one study in 1981, a gentle guide dog named Honey went to live in a nursing home in Melbourne, Australia. Six months later, the **effects** on the residents were clear. The 60 residents were happier, more active, and more **optimistic** about life.

Therapy animals must be **calm** and gentle. They must enjoy people and feel comfortable with people that they do not know. Because there are often other pets in these programs, the dogs must be friendly with other pets. All therapy animals must be clean and **up-to-date** with their vaccinations.

Read each statement. Circle *T* for *True* or *F* for *False*.

1. In pet therapy programs, patients can visit with their pets.   T   F
2. Many therapy pets live in hospitals.   T   F
3. Pets sometimes help people talk about their lives.   T   F
4. Pets can help patients reduce stress.   T   F
5. Some studies show the positive effects of pet therapy.   T   F
6. Animals in this program have the vaccinations they need.   T   F
7. Some therapy dogs bark a lot.   T   F

Match the definitions below with a word in bold face from the reading.

1. related to the body   _____physically_____

2. relaxed   _____

3. current   _____

4. related to feelings   _____

5. positive   _____

6. results   _____

7. lower   _____

4 The States

Practicing on Your Own

1. Circle the correct noun.

1. Chicago is one of the largest **city / cities** in the United States.
2. Many of the **visitor / visitors** take the city tour.
3. Every **farm / farms** needs a tractor.
4. Death Valley is one of the hottest **desert / deserts** in the United States.
5. There are many **seaport / seaports** on the east coast.
6. Each **state / states** has a state flag.
7. My cousin lives on one of the Hawaiian **island / islands**.
8. Many big **city / cities** receive a lot of **visitor / visitors**.
9. Every **tourist / tourists** takes photographs of this beautiful park.
10. All of the national **park / parks** are busy in the summer.

2. Complete these sentences with the correct form of the verb in parentheses.

1. A glacier (be) _____is_____ a river of frozen ice.
2. A forest (have) _____ many trees.
3. Many large cities (have) _____ seaports.
4. Most mountain ranges (run) _____ from north to south.
5. Farmers in the south (grow) _____ oranges and grapefruit.
6. A valley (be) _____ a low, flat area between mountain ranges.
7. Many tourists (travel) _____ in the summer.
8. A desert (receive) _____ very little rain.
9. Many ships (enter) _____ the seaport every day.
10. Millions of tourists (visit) _____ that city every year.
11. The river (supply) _____ the city's drinking water.
12. The Great Lakes (lie) _____ between Canada and the United States.

3. Answer these questions about the map of the United States.

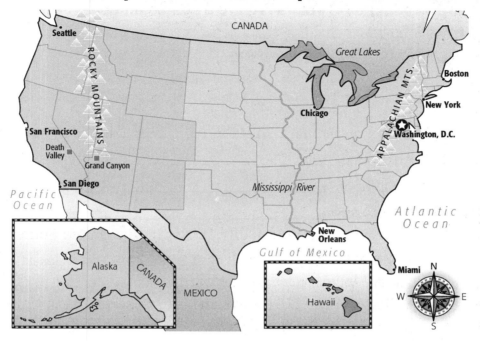

Yes, there is. No, there isn't.	Yes, there are. No, there aren't.	Yes, it is. No, it isn't.	Yes, they are. No, they aren't.

1. Are there 50 states in the United States? _____ Yes, there are. _____
2. Is Washington, D.C. the capital? _____
3. Are there six Great Lakes? _____
4. Is Chicago on one of the lakes? _____
5. Is Hawaii a group of islands? _____
6. Are Alaska and Hawaii separate from the other states? _____
7. Is Hawaii the largest state? _____
8. Is Boston a seaport? _____
9. Are there many seaports on the east coast? _____
10. Are there many large cities on the coasts? _____
11. Is there a long mountain range in the south? _____
12. Is there a lot of snow in the mountains? _____
13. Is the Mississippi the longest river in the United States? _____
14. Are there five countries in North America? _____
15. Is Mexico north of the United States? _____

4. **Complete these sentences with a noun from the box. Some of the sentences require a count noun; others require a non-count noun. Several answers are possible.**

traffic	tourists	mountain ranges	seaports
rain	boats	pollution	mountains
✓ snow	trees		

1. There is a lot of _____ snow _____ in the mountains.

2. There isn't much _____ in the desert.

3. There are a lot of _____ on the Mississippi River.

4. There are many _____ in the national parks in the summer.

5. There aren't many _____ in a desert.

6. There are many excellent _____ along the coast.

7. Florida is a flat state. There aren't any _____ in Florida.

8. There are several long _____ in the west.

9. There is a lot of _____ in a large city.

10. The air in the country is clean. There isn't a lot of _____ in the country.

5. **Complete these sentences with *there is/isn't* or *there are/aren't* and *a lot of, many,* or *much.***

1. There are a lot of factories in that city, so _____ there is a lot of _____ pollution.

2. That area receives very little rain, so _____ there isn't much _____ farming.

3. There are many colleges in that city, so _____ bookstores.

4. There is a lot of traffic in that city, so _____ noise.

5. That area receives very little rain, so _____ farms.

6. The population of that city is very low, so _____ traffic.

7. There are many large companies in that city, so _____ unemployment.

8. There is a lot of snow in the mountains, so _____ ski resorts.

9. That island is rainy and cold, so _____ tourists.

10. There are many immigrants in that city, so _____ ethnic restaurants.

11. The soil is rich, so _____ farms.

6. Complete these questions and answers about North Carolina. Begin each question with *How much* or *How many*.

1. How <u>many cities and towns are there in North Carolina</u>?

There are more than 500 cities and towns in North Carolina.

2. How _____?

There are 63 state parks.

3. How _____?

There are 75 public and 47 private colleges and universities.

4. How _____?

There is a lot of rain, about 50 inches (127 cm) a year.

5. How _____?

There is a lot of tourism, especially along the coast and in the mountains.

6. How _____?

There are one or two hurricanes in North Carolina every year.

7. How _____?

There is a lot of traffic in the large cities.

8. How _____?

There are 301 miles (484 km) of coastline.

9. How _____?

There is a lot of farming. Two major crops are sweet potatoes and tobacco.

Listening

7. First, look at the map. Then, listen and complete the information about Florida.

Population: _____
　Hispanic: _____%
　African-American: _____%
　Senior citizens: _____%
Weather
　Summer _____
　　Average temperature in July: _____
　Winter _____
　　Average temperature in January: _____
　　Average rainfall: _____ inches
Economy
　Farming: _____
　_____
　Tourism: _____
　_____

8. Listen and circle the correct answers.

1. **a.** in the northeast　　**b.** in the southwest　　**c.** in the southeast
2. **a.** Key West　　　　　**b.** the Florida Keys　　**c.** Miami
3. **a.** Tallahassee　　　　**b.** Miami　　　　　　**c.** Jacksonville
4. **a.** 2,800,000　　　　**b.** 16,000,000　　　**c.** 280,000,000
5. **a.** 15%　　　　　　　**b.** 17%　　　　　　　**c.** 18%
6. **a.** senior citizens　　**b.** African-Americans　**c.** Hispanics
7. **a.** Sunshine State　　**b.** Senior Citizen State　**c.** Vacation State
8. **a.** 54″ a year　　　　**b.** 60″ a year　　　　**c.** 81″ a year
9. **a.** 54°　　　　　　　**b.** 60°　　　　　　　**c.** 81°
10. **a.** tomatoes　　　　**b.** cotton　　　　　　**c.** oranges
11. **a.** manufacturing　　**b.** tourism　　　　　**c.** farming

9. Listen to the questions and write the correct short answers about Florida.

1. _No, it isn't._
2. _____
3. _____
4. _____
5. _____

6. _____
7. _____
8. _____
9. _____
10. _____

Reading: Alaska and Hawaii

Alaska and Hawaii were the last two states to become part of the United States. They are the only two states separated from the continental United States. Alaska became part of the United States on January 3, 1959, and Hawaii entered seven months later on August 21, 1959.

Alaska is located far to the north, separated from the United States by Canada. There is water on three sides of the state. Alaska is the largest state, but it has one of the smallest populations, with only 630,000 residents. It is also the coldest state; the average winter temperature is 5°. Millions of people visit Alaska every year to see the bears, moose, whales, and other wildlife; to climb the highest mountains in the country; and to fish in its cold rivers. Tourism, oil, and fishing are Alaska's major industries.

Hawaii is located in the Pacific Ocean, about 2,400 miles from the west coast. It is a group of 132 islands, formed by volcanoes millions of years ago. Most of the islands are very small. The majority of the population—1,200,000 people—lives on eight main islands. Warm weather and beautiful beaches have made tourism Hawaii's main industry.

Read and check (✓) *Hawaii* or *Alaska*. For some statements, both states are correct.

	Alaska	Hawaii
1. This is the largest state.	✓	❑
2. This state has a lot of oil.	❑	❑
3. This state is located in the ocean.	❑	❑
4. This is the newest state.	❑	❑
5. This state is warm most of the year.	❑	❑
6. This state is very cold in the winter.	❑	❑
7. This state is separated from the continental United States.	❑	❑
8. Tourism is a major industry in this state.	❑	❑
9. I would like to visit this state.	❑	❑

Computers and the Internet

Practicing on Your Own

1. Label the picture. Write the words from the box.

| CD-ROM |
| floppy disk |
| monitor |
| keyboard |
| keys |
| speakers |
| mouse |
| mouse pad |
| screen |

2. Complete the sentence with the words from Exercise 1.

1. I think my _____mouse_____ is broken. I can't move the text on the screen.

2. I'm typing on the _____.

3. I need to replace my _____. The picture is not clear.

4. I'm trying to save my paper on a _____ _____disk_____, but it's not working. What's wrong?

5. This is a 15″ flat _____ monitor. I would like to buy a larger one, maybe a 17″ or a 20″ one.

6. I'm putting a _____ into the computer. Now I can listen to some music.

7. There's a problem with the _____. I can't hear the music.

8. I'm moving the mouse on the _____ _____.

9. I'm reading the instruction manual for my computer. I don't know how to use all of the _____ on the keyboard.

3. Look at the pictures and complete the sentences. Write the present continuous form of the verbs in parentheses.

I am **sending** an e-mail.	I am **not mailing** a letter.
You **are sending** an e-mail.	You **aren't mailing** an e-mail.
We **are sending** an e-mail.	We **aren't mailing** letters.
They **are sending** an e-mail.	They **aren't mailing** letters.
He **is sending** a letter.	He **isn't mailing** a letter.
It **is working** well.	It **isn't working** well.

1. Sheila _____ is using _____ (use) a PDA, a hand-held computer.

2. She _____ (check) her schedule for the day.

3. She _____ (change) an appointment.

4. She _____ (save) the changes.

5. Patrick _____ (take/not) pictures with a traditional camera.

6. He _____ (use) a digital camera so that he can see the pictures immediately.

7. He _____ still _____ (learn) to use all of the features of the camera.

8. He _____ (turn/not) on the flash because there is enough light.

9. Eduardo and Miranda _____ (plan) a trip to Boston.

10. They _____ (ask/not) a travel agent for help.

11. They _____ (make) all of the plans by themselves.

12. They _____ (search) the Internet for information.

4. Tense contrast. Look at the pictures and complete the sentences. Write the present continuous or the simple present tense of the verbs in parentheses. Some of the verbs are negative.

I have a computer.	**I don't have** a computer.
You have a computer.	**You don't have** a computer.
We have two computers.	**We don't have** any computers.
They have one computer.	**They don't have** a computer.
She has a computer.	**She doesn't have** a new computer.
It works very well.	**It doesn't work** well.

1. So Jung _____works_____ (work) for a software company.

2. Today, she _____isn't working_____ (work/not) at her office.

3. She _____ (work) at home.

4. She's at home today because she _____ (have) a bad cold.

5. The students _____ (use) the computers in the lab.

6. One student _____ (check) her e-mail.

7. The other student _____ (listen) to a dialogue.

8. The students _____ (go) to the computer lab every Saturday morning.

9. Mohammed _____ (spend) time in the computer lab twice a week.

10. Today, he _____ (practice) grammar.

11. He _____ (like) to use the computers in the lab because he _____ _____ (have/not) a computer at home.

5. Tense contrast. Complete the sentences with the present continuous or the simple present tense. Use a negative form when necessary.

1. I _____ (work) full-time. I _____ (work) right now.

2. My classmates and I _____ (learn) English.

3. I _____ (listen) to music right now.

4. My English class _____ (meet) on Saturday.

5. The students in my class _____ (come) from the same country.

6. Write questions in the present continuous tense using the cues. Then, answer the questions. Use your imagination. Add other words to complete the questions.

1. Megan / use / computer / ?

   <u>Is Megan using a computer?</u>

   <u>Yes, she is.</u>

2. she / work / at her desk / ?

   _____

   _____

3. why / she / sit / on her bed / ?

   _____

   _____

4. what / she / type / ?

   _____

   _____

5. Jim's grandparents / look at / new computers / ?

   _____

   _____

6. who / help / them / ?

   _____

   _____

Listening

7. Listen and (circle) the correct answers.

Conversation 1

1. They are at . . .

   a. a library.　　　**b.** a supermarket.　　　**c.** the White House.　　　**d.** work.

2. The man is talking to . . .

   a. his wife.　　　**b.** a cashier.　　　**c.** a librarian.　　　**d.** a security guard.

3. What is he looking for?

   a. information　　　**b.** a newspaper　　　**c.** a book　　　**d.** a computer

Conversation 2

1. They are at . . .

   a. school.　　　**b.** an airport.　　　**c.** a bus stop.　　　**d.** work.

2. The man and the woman are . . .

   a. co-workers.　　　**b.** brother and sister.　　　**c.** passengers.　　　**d.** customers.

3. What is the woman doing?

   a. checking her e-mail　　　**b.** writing a report　　　**c.** searching the Internet

4. What kind of computer is she using?

   a. a desktop computer　　　**b.** a laptop computer　　　**c.** a hand-held computer

8. Look at the picture. Listen and answer the questions.

1. **Three people are waiting.**
2. _____
3. _____
4. _____
5. _____
6. _____
7. _____
8. _____

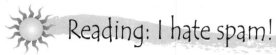

Reading: I hate spam!

You open your mailbox and find bills, letters, important notices, and junk mail. You throw away the junk mail—advertisements, real estate notices, or credit card applications. Today, there's another annoying type of junk mail. It's called *spam*. Spam is unwanted, uninvited e-mail messages.

Spam has become a serious problem for computer users. In one day, a person may receive 20 or more spam messages. Spam may include the following:

- offers to make money fast
- offers of health products
- advertisements

Spam is very cheap for the companies or individuals who use it to advertise. They can send thousands of messages per hour. The problem is for you, the receiver of the spam. Spam takes up space on your computer. It takes time for you to delete the spam. All computer users know that it often takes time to open e-mail. The more messages you have, the longer it takes. If many of the messages are spam, you waste time.

How can you reduce or prevent spam? Many people install software to block spam. Or, you can use a temporary e-mail address. For example, start a free account on the Internet. Don't use your real name as part of the e-mail, such as rickyvasquez@myhome.com. Cancel the account after a short time and start a new one. An idea for someone with a Web site is to leave off the e-mail address from the Web site. Finally, it is very important to read everything on the Internet carefully, especially if you are filling out a form. It is often necessary to click a box to keep your name off of a new list for advertisers.

Fortunately for computer users, computer companies are writing new software to help reduce and block spam.

Answer the questions.

1. What is spam? Find and <u>underline</u> the definition in the reading.

2. Which is **not** an example of spam? Circle your answer.
   a. an advertisement for vitamins   **b.** a message from your friend
   c. a travel offer

3. Why is spam good for companies? Circle your answer.
   a. It's expensive.   **b.** It takes a lot of time.   **c.** It's cheap.

4. How many suggestions can you find to reduce or prevent spam?

6 A Healthy Lifestyle

1. What suggestions do you have for each health problem below? Write the number of the suggestion under each picture.

chicken pox	sore throat	sprained ankle

Sherri	Liz	Manuel
__2__ ___ ___	___ ___ ___	__1__ ___ ___

1. elevate the leg	**4.** apply lotion	**7.** stay home from school for a week
2. take cool baths	**5.** drink tea	**8.** buy an elastic bandage
3. buy throat lozenges	**6.** use an ice pack	**9.** gargle with salt and warm water

2. Answer the questions about each person in Exercise 1.

1. What is Sherri going to do?
   She is going to take cool baths.

2. How long is she going to stay home from school?
   _____

3. What is her mother going to apply to Sherri's face and body?
   _____

4. What is Liz going to drink?
   _____

5. What is Liz going to gargle with?
   _____

6. What is Manuel going to buy?
   _____

7. What is Manuel going to put on his ankle?
   _____

3. Answer these questions about Ayumi. She is in bed with the flu and a temperature of 103°.

Ayumi

| Yes, she does. |
| No, she doesn't. |

| Yes, she is. |
| No, she isn't. |

1. Does Ayumi have the flu? _____ Yes, she does. _____

2. Is she going to go to work today? _____

3. Is she going to call the doctor? _____

4. Does Ayumi have a fever? _____

5. Does she have a toothache? _____

6. Is she going to take some aspirin? _____

7. Is she going to sleep a lot today? _____

8. Is she going to go to school tonight? _____

9. Does she feel terrible? _____

10. Is she going to drink a lot of fluids? _____

4. Complete these questions about your health with *Do* or *Are*. Then, answer the questions.

1. _____ Are _____ you often tired? _____

2. _____ you drink six or more glasses of water a day? _____

3. _____ you overweight? _____

4. _____ you often get sick? _____

5. _____ you see the dentist at least once a year? _____

6. _____ you a smoker? _____

7. _____ you under a lot of stress? _____

8. _____ you often feel depressed? _____

9. _____ you eat a lot of fried foods? _____

10. _____ you exercise regularly? _____

5. Complete these questions with the correct question words from the box. You can use some of the words more than once.

How many	How much	How long	How high
When	How long	What kind of	Which

1. _____How long_____ are you going to be in the hospital?

2. _____ am I going to feel better?

3. _____ stitches is she going to need?

4. _____ specialist are you going to see?

5. _____ pounds is he going to lose?

6. _____ is she going to be in that cast?

7. _____ days is he going to be in the hospital?

8. _____ vaccines are we going to need to travel?

9. _____ is that medical test going to cost?

10. _____ is his temperature?

6. Complete this conversation.

Kate: Amy! You look wonderful! Congratulations!

Amy: Thank you.

Kate: _When are you due?_____

Amy: I'm due on October 27.

Kate: _____?

Amy: We're going to have a boy.

Kate: _____?

Amy: We're going to name him Josh.

Kate: I love that name! _____?

Amy: Yes, my husband is going to take two weeks off from work.

Kate: _____?

Amy: Yes, I am. I'm going to take maternity leave for three months.

Kate: _____?

Amy: My mom is going to take care of him when I go back to work.

7. Rewrite these sentences. Use *it, him, her,* or *them* for the <u>underlined</u> words.

1. I'll visit <u>Maria</u> in the hospital.   I'll visit her in the hospital.

2. I'll take <u>my father</u> to the doctor.   I'll take him to the doctor.

3. I'll send <u>flowers</u> to Sandra.   I'll send them to Sandra.

4. I'll take <u>this medication</u> for a week.   I'll take it for a week.

5. I'll help <u>my parents</u>.   I'll help them.

6. I'll send <u>Jack</u> a get-well card.   I'll send him a get-well card.

7. I'll get <u>an ice pack</u> for you.   I'll get it for you.

8. I'll need these <u>crutches</u> for a week.   I'll need them for a week.
   muletas

9. I'll call <u>my boss</u>.   I'll call him.

10. I'll speak to <u>the doctor</u>.   I'll speak to him.

8. Answer each question twice. Show that you are not certain of the answer. In the first answer, use *will* and *probably*. In the second answer, use *may* or *might*.

1. What kind of diet will she need?   (a low-fat diet)   *will*

   She'll probably need a low-fat diet.

   She might need a low-fat diet.

2. When will the doctor operate?   (tomorrow)

   He'll probably operate tomorrow.

   He may operate tomorrow.

3. What kind of test will you need?   (a blood test)

   _____

   _____

4. What will the doctor prescribe?   (antibiotics)

   _____

   _____

5. What will the dentist do?   (extract the tooth)

   _____

   _____

9. You will hear nine sentences. Write each sentence next to the picture it refers to.

1. _____

2. _____

3. _____

4. The doctor is taking the man's blood pressure.

5. _____

6. _____

7. _____

8. _____

9. _____

10. Listen to each conversation. Then, answer the questions.

Conversation 1

1. What kind of a doctor is this woman seeing? _____ an allergist _____

2. What is she allergic to? _____

3. When does she need the medication? _____

4. What shouldn't she eat? _____

Conversation 2

5. What is Mr. Jackson's cholesterol level? _____

6. How old is Mr. Jackson? _____

7. What are three causes of Mr. Jackson's medical problems?

_____

8. What kind of diet does Mr. Jackson need? _____

9. What kind of test is the nurse going to schedule? _____

11. Listen and write short answers about your lifestyle.

1. _____   6. _____
2. _____   7. _____
3. _____   8. _____
4. _____   9. _____
5. _____   10. _____

Reading: Diabetes

When Diana went for her regular physical checkup, she told her doctor that she felt tired and that she was always thirsty. Her doctor suggested a blood test for diabetes. The results came back positive. Diana had Type 2 diabetes.

Over 17 million people in the United States suffer from Type 2 diabetes. In the beginning, the symptoms are often mild. People with diabetes report that they feel tired, are often thirsty, and need to urinate frequently. Diana had many of the common risk factors, too. She was over 45 and had high blood pressure. Diana was 60 pounds overweight, but she did not exercise. Diana is Hispanic, and diabetes is especially high in minority populations, including the African-American, Hispanic, Asian, and Native-American communities.

Type 2 diabetes is the most common form of diabetes. In Type 2 diabetes, the body does not produce enough insulin or does not use insulin effectively. People with diabetes need to watch their blood-sugar levels carefully. In time, diabetes can damage the circulatory system, the nervous system, and major organs of the body. It can cause blindness, kidney disease, and heart disease.

Type 2 diabetes is easy to diagnose with a blood test. It can often be controlled by proper diet and regular exercise. People with diabetes must usually reduce fats and carbohydrates and control their sugar intake.

At first, Diana needed to take diabetes medication. She began to walk and now walks four miles a day. Over the past year, she lost 50 pounds. Her diabetes is now under control, and she no longer needs to take medication for the disease.

Read the statements and circle *T* for *True* or *F* for *False*.

1. Many people with diabetes don't know that they have this disease.   (T)   F
2. Most people with Type 2 diabetes are under 45 years old.   T   F
3. Type 2 diabetes is more common in minority populations.   T   F
4. Diabetes can damage the kidneys.   T   F
5. A blood test can show if a person has diabetes.   T   F
6. People with diabetes must carefully control their diets.   T   F
7. All people with diabetes must take medication.   T   F

People and Places

Practicing on Your Own

1. Complete the sentences comparing the people in the pictures. Use the adjectives from the boxes.

Anne   Kathy

straight	curly	neat	sloppy	tall

1. Anne's hair is ___straighter than___ Kathy's.

2. Kathy's hair is _____ Anne's.

3. Anne is _____ Kathy.

4. Kathy is _____ Anne.

5. Kathy is _____ Anne.

STEVEN   MIKE

thin	heavy	athletic	a good student

1. Steven is _____ Mike.

2. Mike is _____ Steven.

3. Mike is _____ Steven.

4. Steven is _____ Mike.

hardworking	talkative	sociable	healthy

1. José is _____ Olivia.

2. Olivia is _____ José.

3. Olivia is _____ José.

4. José is _____ Olivia.

2. Write new sentences comparing the people in the pictures on page 38. Use the adjectives in parentheses and *as . . . as* or *not as . . . as*.

> **as . . . as / not as . . . as**
> Anne's hair is *as dark as* Kathy's.
> Kathy is *not as neat as* Anne.

1. Anne is _____ not as tall as _____ Kathy. (tall)
2. Mike is _____ not as thin as _____ Steven. (thin)
3. Steven is _____ not as athletic as _____ Mike. (athletic)
4. José is _____ not as relaxed as _____ Olivia. (relaxed)
5. Olivia is _____ not as serious as _____ José. (serious)
6. José is _____ not as friendly as _____ Olivia. (friendly)

3. Your opinion. Write questions using the cues and *as . . . as*. Then, answer the questions.

1. subway train / bus / fast
   Is a subway train as fast as a bus?
   A subway train is faster than a bus.

2. walking / running / healthy
   _____
   _____

3. going to the movies / going to the symphony / enjoyable
   _____
   _____

4. police work / military work / dangerous
   _____
   _____

5. tennis / soccer / exciting
   _____
   _____

6. living in the city / living in the suburbs / comfortable
   _____
   _____

4. **Look at the picture of two waitresses. Read the information in the boxes about their job experience.**

Kelly
20 years old
1 year experience
Absences from
 work: 20 times
Tips per day: $60
Breaks per day: 4

Milly
55 years old
35 years experience
Absences from work:
 10 times
Tips per day: $100
Breaks per day: 2

old	young	experienced	careful
good	friendly	earns more/fewer tips	takes breaks more/less often
			is absent more/less often

Write sentences comparing Kelly and Milly. Use the comparative form, *as . . . as*, or *not as . . . as*, and the adjectives/phrases from the box.

1. Kelly is not as old as Milly.
2. _____
3. _____
4. _____
5. _____
6. _____
7. _____
8. _____
9. _____

5. Read the charts about two neighborhoods. Then, write a paragraph answering the question, "Which neighborhood do you want to live in?" Try to use some comparative adjectives in your paragraph.

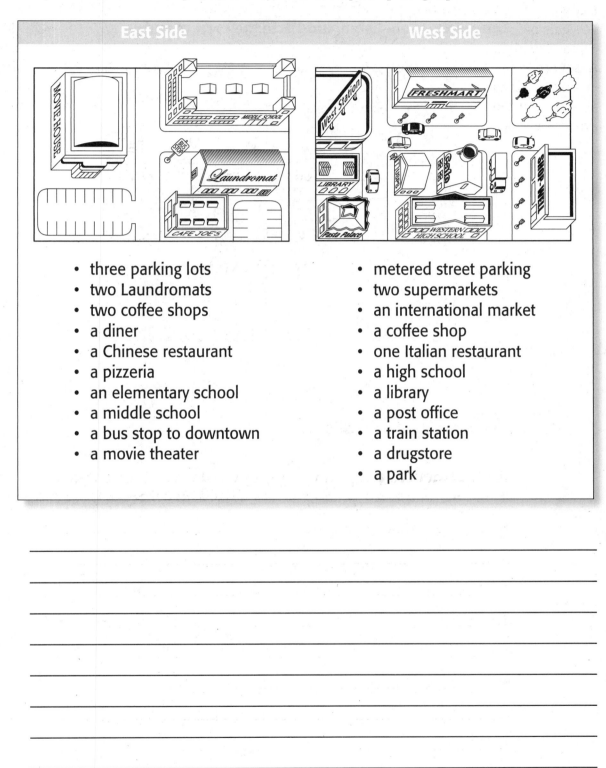

East Side	West Side
• three parking lots	• metered street parking
• two Laundromats	• two supermarkets
• two coffee shops	• an international market
• a diner	• a coffee shop
• a Chinese restaurant	• one Italian restaurant
• a pizzeria	• a high school
• an elementary school	• a library
• a middle school	• a post office
• a bus stop to downtown	• a train station
• a movie theater	• a drugstore
	• a park

_____

_____

_____

_____

_____

_____

_____

_____

_____

6. **Read the chart about two cities—Cleveland, Ohio and New Orleans, Louisiana. Then, listen and circle the correct answers.**

	Cleveland, Ohio	New Orleans, Louisiana
Days above 90°	12	67
Days below 35°	123	13
Snow	55.4"	.2"
Rain	36.6"	62"
Family restaurants	36	67
Professional sports teams	5	3
Symphonies	9	2
Art museums	5	4

1. Cleveland   New Orleans   5. Cleveland   New Orleans

2. Cleveland   New Orleans   6. Cleveland   New Orleans

3. Cleveland   New Orleans   7. Cleveland   New Orleans

4. Cleveland   New Orleans   8. Cleveland   New Orleans

7. **Listen to the conversations.**

Conversation 1: Complete the sentences.

Maggie: *The Matrix* was a great movie, wasn't it?

John: Are you kidding? *Star Wars* was _____.

Maggie: No way, John. *The Matrix* was _____.

John: It was interesting, Maggie, but it wasn't _____ _____ *Star Wars*.

Maggie: Oh, it was _____, and the acting was much better. But, *Star Wars* had more spectacular special effects.

John: So, you agree with me. *Star Wars* was _____ *The Matrix*.

Maggie: You didn't hear anything I said!

Conversation 2: Circle the adjectives that describe the <u>mother's</u> soup.

  a. saltier   **c.** thinner   **e.** not as spicy   **g.** tastier

  b. not as salty   **d.** thicker   **f.** spicier   **h.** not as tasty

42   Unit 7

Reading: Two Hotel Careers

The hotel clerk is one of the first persons that guests see when they check into a hotel. The clerk at the front desk welcomes the guests. Hotel clerks must be polite and helpful. They must be able to answer questions about the hotel and general questions about the area where the hotel is located. A hotel clerk has to work quickly and correctly, taking reservations and reviewing hotel bills. This job also requires clerks to deal with problems—one of the most difficult parts of the job. Hotel clerks in tourist areas deal with large groups of tourists and may have to work long hours and overtime.

Hotel clerks often start at the hotels in other positions such bellhops or porters. They must have good communication skills and a strong educational background. A college degree may be required for some hotels.

The schedules for clerks vary depending on the type of hotel. They have flexible work schedules, but often work weekends and evenings. The average salary is $15,000, but the salary can be higher according to the location, size, and type of hotel.

A good hotel chef can attract more guests. Chefs are responsible for supervising the work of the kitchen cooks and food preparation workers. They order supplies and help plan and write menus. In a large hotel, there may be several chefs, each in charge of a different job such as vegetables or sauces. The responsibilities depend on the type of restaurant in which they work. Being a chef can be stressful. Chefs must work with a team. They must be able to stand for many hours and must be strong and able to lift heavy pots, often filled with hot liquid. They have to work near hot ovens and grills. Burns and cuts are common injuries.

Most chefs have high school diplomas with some courses in business or management in addition to many years of experience as cooks. Many attend special colleges or institute programs that take from one to three years to complete and work in a variety of places to gain experience.

Like hotel clerks, the schedules for hotel chefs vary. Chefs can expect to work early mornings, late evenings, holidays, and weekends. There are also many opportunities for part-time work. The average salary is about $23,175, but the salary may be higher or lower depending on the hotel and the responsibilities.

Read the statements and circle T for *True* or F for *False*.

1. A hotel clerk has more contact with the hotel guests.   (T)   F

2. A hotel chef has more supervisory responsibilities.   T   F

3. Working with people is an important part of both jobs.   T   F

4. Both jobs have a variety of schedules.   T   F

5. A hotel chef makes more decisions than a hotel clerk.   T   F

6. A hotel chef's job is more stressful than a hotel clerk's.   T   F

7. A hotel chef's job requires more strength than a hotel clerk's.   T   F

8. A hotel clerk has a safer job than a hotel chef.   T   F

8 Moving

Practicing on Your Own

1. Marco's move. Put the verbs in parentheses in the past tense.

Marco and his family _____**lived**_____ (live) in New York.
Marco _____ (be) an assistant manager for a
large telephone company. A few months ago, the company
_____ (offer) him a promotion. They _____
(ask) him to move to Ohio because they _____
(need) a bilingual manager for their Cleveland office. His wife
_____ (be) unhappy because her family _____
(live) in New York, but she _____ (agree) to move.
   When Marco and his wife _____ (arrive) in Ohio, they
_____ (be) surprised at the cost of houses. Houses _____
(be) much less than in New York! They _____ (look) at many
houses. They _____ (like) a three-bedroom home in a small
town near Cleveland. They _____ (apply) for a mortgage and
only _____ (wait) three weeks for the approval. They
_____ (move) in last month. They are very happy with the
schools and the neighborhood.

2. A great landlord. Explain what the landlord did before the new tenants moved in. Use one of the phrases from the box.

replace/stove	call/exterminator	✓ repair
fix	put in/new carpet	install/new lock
install/new light	paint	clean

1. The faucet leaked.   **He repaired it.** _____
2. The carpet was old and dirty.   _____
3. The stove was old.   _____
4. The air conditioner was broken.   _____
5. The kitchen cabinets were dirty.   _____
6. The paint in the bedroom was peeling. _____
7. The lock was broken.   _____
8. There were ants in the kitchen.   _____
9. The hall was dark.   _____

44   UNIT 8

3. Complete these statements about your childhood. All of the verbs are irregular. You might need to use the negative in some of your sentences.

> I grew up in the city.
> I didn't grow up in the city.

1. I _____ up in the city. (grow)

2. We _____ our neighbors. (know)

3. I _____ a lot of friends. (have)

4. I _____ school when I was five years old. (begin)

5. I _____ to a private school. (go)

6. I _____ a uniform to school. (wear)

7. My family _____ a car. (have)

8. We _____ a vacation every year. (take)

9. My father _____ me how to drive. (teach)

10. I _____ my country when I was a teenager. (leave)

4. Look at the pictures and answer the questions about Stan's decision to come to the United States. Use your imagination for some of the answers.

2001   2002

1. Where did Stan live?
   Stan lived in Poland. _____

2. When did he get his visa?
   _____

3. How did his parents feel?
   _____

4. When did Stan leave Poland?
   _____

5. What city did he fly to?
   _____

6. Who met him at the airport?
   _____

5. Complete these sentences about your childhood with was/wasn't or were/weren't.

1. My home _____ in the city.

2. My home _____ large.

3. It _____ near town.

4. It _____ near public transportation.

5. There _____ many good restaurants in my area.

6. There _____ a school nearby.

7. There _____ a lot of children in my neighborhood.

8. The elementary school _____ near my house.

9. My neighbors _____ friendly.

10. My neighborhood _____ safe.

11. My neighborhood _____ quiet.

6. Mr. Charles doesn't like his new tenants. Read the statements about the new tenants. Compare them with the old tenants.

1. His new tenants play loud music.
    The old tenants didn't play loud music. _____

2. His new tenants give loud parties.
    _____

3. His new tenants watch TV all night.
    _____

4. His new tenants pay the rent late.
    _____

5. His new tenants leave all the lights on when they go out.
    _____

6. His new tenants damaged the carpet.
    _____

7. His new tenants have loud arguments.
    _____

8. His new tenants are loud.
    _____

7. **Tense contrast.** Complete this story about Nelson and Helena's move. Use the present, present continuous, future, or past.

Time to Move

Last year, Nelson and Helena _____ (decide) to move to a new apartment. They _____ (like) their old neighborhood, but their apartment _____ (be) too small. They _____ (need) more bedrooms. They _____ (look) for about a month and _____ (find) an apartment in a two-family house near town, but they only _____ (see) the neighborhood in the daytime, never at night.

Nelson and Helena and their family _____ now _____ (live) in the new apartment. They _____ (move) in four months ago. This time, they _____ (love) the apartment. It's on the first floor and it _____ (have) three bed-rooms and two bathrooms. The landlord always _____ (fix) any-thing that's broken. Last month, Nelson _____ (be) two days late with the rent, but the landlord _____ (say-negative) anything.

But, Nelson and Helena _____ (hate) their new neighbor-hood. In the daytime, it's quiet, but at night, it's a different story. Teenagers and young men _____ (stand) on the street corner and _____ (talk) loudly. Cars _____ (drive) up and down the street with their stereos very loud. When Helena _____ (come) home at night, she _____ (feel-negative) safe walking from the parking lot to the building. Last week, someone _____ (break) into their car and _____ (steal) the stereo. so now, Helena wants to move again and Nelson _____ (feel) the same way. When their lease _____ (end), they _____ (look) for a new apartment. This time, they _____ (check) it out in the day and in the evening.

Listening

8. Listen and complete these answers with a verb in the past tense.

1. She _____came_____ in 2001.
2. He _____ $2,000.
3. I _____ one in Dallas.
4. Her cousins _____ her.
5. He _____ one in a hotel.
6. He _____ with his uncle.
7. He _____ for one in 1997.
8. He _____ it in 2000.

9. Yes, he _____.
10. No, I _____.
11. I _____ at an adult school.
12. I _____ classes for three years.
13. No, I _____.
14. I _____ it in 2003.
15. My sister _____ me.
16. She _____ $3,000.

9. Listen to this conversation. Read the questions and check (✓) the correct answer. It is possible to check both.

	David	Maria
1. Who had a difficult first year in the United States?	☑	❑
2. Who came to the United States in 1999?	❑	❑
3. Who studied English before coming to the United States?	❑	❑
4. Who went to school at night?	❑	❑
5. Who worked in a parking lot?	❑	❑
6. Who lived with a friend?	❑	❑
7. Who had family in the United States?	❑	❑
8. Who needed a license to work?	❑	❑
9. Who studied English for four years?	❑	❑
10. Who had an easier experience?	❑	❑

10. Listen to the conversation. Then, answer the questions in a complete sentence.

1. When did Bill and Susan move?
   They moved last weekend.

2. Where did they move to?
   _____

3. Where did they live before they moved?
   _____

4. Why did they move?
   _____

5. Did Bill want to move?

_____

6. Why was Susan happy about the move?

_____

7. When is the speaker going to visit his brother and sister-in-law?

_____

Reading: The Housing Market

It is the dream of most families—a home of their own. In the year 2000, 68% of families owned their own homes. How affordable is this wish?

A look at the housing market in the United States shows some surprising differences in housing prices. For example, on the west coast, the median home price is $214,100. In the Midwest, the price is much less, about $136,000. In the South, an average home is $147,000, and in the Northeast, an average home is $164,300. Housing prices are based on supply and demand. How many houses are there? How many people are looking for a house? In areas with strong economies and many high-paying jobs, houses are more expensive. Housing near large cities such as San Francisco, Washington, D.C., Boston, and New York, is much higher than housing in small cities and towns.

The average apartment rental in the United States in 2000 was $602. The average monthly payment for a mortgage was $1088. New mortgage payments, those obtained in the last five years, are much higher. When interest rates are low, more people buy houses because mortgages are less expensive. When interest rates are high, it is much more expensive to buy a house.

How much should a family spend on housing? Banks and lenders recommend that housing costs should be 35% or less of a family's monthly income. However, some families are now spending almost 50% of their monthly income on a home of their own.

Read the statement and circle T for *True* or F for *False*.

1. Thirty percent of people in the United States own their own homes.   T (F)
2. Houses in the Northeast are the most expensive in the United States.   T F
3. More people live in homes than in apartments.   T F
4. Home prices throughout the United States are similar.   T F
5. Houses in the West are more expensive than houses in the Midwest.   T F
6. A house near the city is usually more expensive than a house in
   a small town.   T F
7. It's more expensive to buy a house than to live in an apartment.   T F
8. The average apartment rental in the United States is $1088 a month.   T F
9. When interest rates are high, mortgages are less expensive.   T F
10. People should spend 35% of their income or less on housing.   T F

9 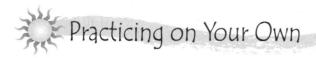 Natural Disasters

Practicing on Your Own

1. Complete each sentence with *was* or *were*. Then, write the name of the natural disaster that the sentence is describing.

| blizzard | hurricane | tornado | flood |
| drought | earthquake | heat wave | forest fire |

1. There ___was___ three feet of snow.   ___blizzard___

2. The temperature _____ over 100° for 20 days.   _____

3. It _____ 7.5 on the Richter scale.   _____

4. Thousands of acres _____ on fire. The flames _____ over 100 feet high.   _____

5. There _____ no rain for six months.   _____

6. The winds _____ over 120 miles an hour.   _____

7. There _____ two large, dark clouds in the sky.   _____

8. The water _____ ten feet deep. Our house _____ under water.   _____

2. Complete these questions with *How* and one of the words from the box.

| heavy | difficult | far | high | small |
| long | deep | windy | wide | strong |

1. _____How high_____ are the mountains?   They're over 10,000 feet.

2. _____ is the next town?   It's about 20 miles.

3. _____ was the water?   It was over our heads.

4. _____ was your test?   It was easy!

5. _____ was the box?   I couldn't pick it up.

6. _____ was the concert?   It was four hours.

7. _____ is the man?   He can lift 200 pounds.

8. _____ is your TV screen?   It's 52″.

9. _____ is your camera?   It fits in my pocket.

10. _____ was it?   My hat blew off.

3. Complete the questions.

> When **did** the river **flood**?   It **flooded** in 2001.
> **Did** you **lose** your home?   No, we **didn't lose** our home.

1. When ___did___ the storm ___begin___?   It began in the morning.
2. How much snow _____ you _____   We had two feet.
3. _____ you _____ to work?   No, we stayed home.
4. _____ your children _____ in the snow?   Yes, they played outside all day.
5. _____ you _____ your driveway?   Yes, we shoveled for two days!
6. How many tornados _____ you _____?   We saw two tornados.
7. _____ you _____ any warning?   We had a five-minute warning.
8. Where _____ you _____?   We hid in our basement.
9. Where _____ the tornado _____?   It hit about two blocks away.
10. _____ it _____ a lot of damage?   Yes, it did a lot of damage.

4. Complete the questions with *did, was,* or *were.*

1. Where ___was___ the flood?
2. How deep _____ the water?
3. _____ you evacuate your house?
4. How _____ you escape?
5. How much damage _____ there?

6. How long _____ the drought?
7. How high _____ the temperature?
8. _____ you get any rain?
9. How _____ you water the crops?
10. _____ any of the cows die?

11. When _____ the volcano explode?
12. _____ you see the explosion?
13. Where _____ you?
14. _____ you lose your home?
15. _____ there any warning of an explosion?

5. Complete the conversation about the storm.

A: _When did the power go out?_

B: The power went out at 5:00 in the evening.

A: _____

B: I was at home.

A: _____

B: Yes, I had a flashlight. And we lit a lot of candles.

A: _____

B: The power was out all night.

A: _____

B: We ate peanut butter and jelly sandwiches.

A: _____

B: Yes, the water worked.

A: _____

B: I went to bed at 9:00.

6. Complete this paragraph with *couldn't* or *had to*.

Last spring we had a terrible flood in my community. It rained for two weeks, and the water in the river began to rise. As the water rose, the radio and TV gave the residents emergency instructions. First, we _____**had to**_____ carry our furniture up to the second floor. We _____ buy emergency supplies, such as food, water, flashlights, and batteries. We also _____ get our important documents together in case we needed to evacuate. The rain continued and the river continued to rise. The children _____ go to school. We _____ drive, except for emergencies. The residents worked together and put sandbags along the river, but we _____ contain the river. Finally, the police gave the order. We _____ evacuate in five hours. We _____ pack our car with clothes, photos, important documents, and some of our electronic equipment. We _____ take everything. Everyone _____ turn off their electricity, gas, and water. We left our home and _____ return for ten days. Thankfully, we only had minor damage.

7. **Tense contrast.** Complete these questions about emergency preparedness. Use the present, present continuous, future, or past tense.

1. What course <u>did he take</u>_____?

    He took a course in CPR (cardiopulmonary resuscitation).

2. The family has to evacuate. Where _____?

    They are going to go to the shelter at the elementary school.

3. Where_____?

    She volunteers at the rescue squad.

4. How much _____?

    She's buying food and water for three days.

5. How many _____?

    She installed four smoke alarms in the house.

6. What _____?

    He's building a safe room under the garage.

7. When _____?

    I'm going to take a first-aid course next month.

8. Where _____?

    My family is going to meet at the hospital in case of an emergency.

9. What number _____?

    He called 911 for emergency help.

10. Where _____?

    We keep emergency supplies in the basement.

11. Where _____?

    Our fire extinguisher is on the wall in the kitchen.

12. When _____?

    I learned the Heimlich maneuver last year.

13. What _____?

    He's looking for batteries for the flashlight.

14. How quickly _____?

    The fire department responded in five minutes.

 Listening

8. **You will hear eight questions about a storm. Write each question next to the correct response.**

1. _____ It began about 6:00 A.M.

2. _____ Yes, they did.

3. _____ Yes, I was an hour late.

4. _____ Yes, there were many trees in the road.

5. _____ It took me two hours.

6. _____ My supervisor couldn't get to work!

7. _How many workers were out?_____ About 50 workers were out.

8. _____ No, it wasn't.

9. **Listen to these instructions given during a heat wave or a drought. Circle the sentence with the same meaning.**

1. (a.) We had to wear light clothing.   **b.** We couldn't wear light clothing.

2. **a.** We had to water our lawns.   **b.** We couldn't water our lawns.

3. **a.** We had to exercise indoors.   **b.** We couldn't exercise indoors.

4. **a.** We had to wash our car at home.   **b.** We couldn't wash our car at home.

5. **a.** We had to drink a lot of water.   **b.** We couldn't drink a lot of water.

6. **a.** We had to turn on the air . conditioner   **b.** We couldn't turn on the air conditioner.

7. **a.** We had to take long showers.   **b.** We couldn't take long showers.

10. **Listen and write the short answers.**

Yes, I am.	No, I'm not.
Yes, I can.	No, I can't.
Yes, I was.	No, I wasn't.

Yes, I do.	No, I don't.
Yes, I did.	No, I didn't.
Yes, I will.	No, I won't.

1. _____   7. _____

2. _____   8. _____

3. _____   9. _____

4. _____   10. _____

5. _____   11. _____

6. _____   12. _____

Reading: Hurricanes

Hurricanes are strong tropical storms. In fact, they are the strongest storms on earth. Hurricanes are violent, circling storms that bring heavy rain, strong winds, and walls of water from the ocean called "storm surges." The center of the hurricane is a calm area called the "eye" of the storm. These violent storms have different names in different parts of the world. In the Atlantic Ocean, they are called hurricanes. In the north Pacific, they are typhoons. In the Indian Ocean and South Pacific, they are called cyclones.

Hurricanes begin in the ocean in late summer or early fall. Hurricanes need warm temperatures and high humidity. As they develop, they begin to spin in a circular pattern. Most hurricanes stay out in the ocean, but a few continue to grow, becoming stronger as they travel west toward land.

Weather forecasters follow storms as they develop and travel in the ocean. When the wind speed of a storm reaches 74 mph, it is called a hurricane. Each hurricane receives a name, given in alphabetical order. For example, storm names for 2003 were Ana, Bill, Claudette, Danny, and so on. Hurricanes travel slowly so that weather stations can give residents warnings several days in advance. Hurricanes do not travel in a straight line, so forecasters are not sure at first where a hurricane is going to hit. A hurricane watch means that a hurricane may hit in 24 to 36 hours. It's a good idea to buy extra batteries, food, and water, and to fill your car with gas. A hurricane warning is more definite. A hurricane will probably hit in the next 24 hours. Prepare your property and house. You may need to evacuate.

The worst hurricane in U. S. history hit Galveston, Texas, in 1900. On September 8, Galveston was a busy seaport of 40,000 residents. By September 9, half the city was under water and 6,000 people were dead. Hurricane Andrew in 1992 was the most expensive hurricane, causing over $25 billion in damage. It completely destroyed the towns of Homestead and Florida City, Florida. In both hurricanes, the wind was violent, but the water caused more damage. The storm surge from the ocean covered marinas, boats, homes, and roads.

Read the statements and (circle) T for *True* or F for *False*.

1. Hurricanes are stronger than tornados.   (T)   F
2. Heavy rain is called a storm surge.   T   F
3. In some parts of the world, a hurricane is known as a typhoon.   T   F
4. Hurricanes often occur in the winter.   T   F
5. All hurricanes cause damage.   T   F
6. Residents have advance notice of a hurricane.   T   F
7. A hurricane watch means there is a possibility of a hurricane.   T   F
8. A hurricane warning is more serious than a hurricane watch.   T   F
9. Half the population of Galveston, Texas died in a 1900 hurricane.   T   F
10. In Hurricane Andrew, the wind caused more damage than the water.   T   F

 # Wedding Plans

1. Complete the sentences with *have to/has to* and one of the phrases from the box.

sit in the front row	hold the rings	throw flowers in the aisle
play good dance music	put a ring on the bride's finger	perform the ceremony
remain quiet during the ceremony	take good pictures	✓ hold the bouquet

1. The bride ___has to___ ___hold the bouquet___.
2. The groom _____ _____.
3. The clergyman _____ _____.
4. The photographer _____ _____.
5. The guests _____ _____.
6. The flower girl _____ _____.
7. The best man _____ _____.
8. The band _____ _____.
9. The parents _____ _____.

2. Nancy and Nick want to have a simple wedding. They are going to get married at City Hall in a civil ceremony with their parents and a few close friends. They are not going to have a big reception. Circle the correct verb form.

1. Nancy and Nick **have to** / **don't have to** get a marriage license.
2. Nancy **has to / doesn't have to** buy an expensive wedding gown.
3. Nancy and Nick **have to / don't have to** exchange rings.
4. Nancy and Nick **have to / don't have to** invite many guests.
5. Nancy **has to / doesn't have to** have a flower girl.
6. Nick **has to / doesn't have to** wear a tuxedo.
7. Nancy and Nick **have to / don't have to** have a photographer.
8. Nancy and Nick **have to / don't have to** design formal invitations.

3. The Grant family is having their daughter, Julia's, wedding in the backyard of their home. Mr. and Mrs. Grant, Julia, and her brother, Will, are helping with the preparations. Read their *to-do* list. (Some things are already done.) Then, write sentences about their busy week.

Who	Task	Finished
1. Mrs. Grant	go to the supermarket	
2. Mr. Grant	fix the lawnmower	✓ yesterday
3. Julia	pick up her gown	✓ a week ago
4. Mrs. Grant	bake the wedding cake	
5. Will	mow the lawn	✓ yesterday afternoon
6. Mr. Grant	wash the cars	
7. Julia	vacuum downstairs	
8. Mr. and Mrs. Grant	pick up Grandma Grant	✓ two days ago
9. Will	take the dog to the neighbor's	
10. Julia and Mrs. Grant	check with the caterer	✓ yesterday
11. Will and Mr. Grant	put up the tents and chairs	
12. Everyone	decorate the backyard	

1. Mrs. Grant *has to go to the supermarket* .

2. Mr. Grant *doesn't have to fix the lawnmower. He fixed it yesterday* .

3. Julia _____ .

4. Mrs. Grant _____ .

5. Will _____ .

6. Mr. Grant _____ .

7. Julia _____ .

8. Mr. and Mrs. Grant _____ .

9. Will _____ .

10. Julia and Mrs. Grant _____ .

11. Will and Mr. Grant _____ .

12. Everyone _____ .

4. Write questions about your country's wedding customs using *have to* and the cues. Add extra words when necessary. Then, answer the questions.

1. couples / have / a civil ceremony / in your country / ?

    Do couples have to have a civil ceremony in your country?

    No, they don't.

2. bride / wear / white gown / ?

    _____

    _____

3. groom / wear / tuxedo / ?

    _____

    _____

4. bride and groom / reserve / wedding hall / many months in advance / ?

    _____

    _____

5. bride's family / pay / wedding and reception / ?

    _____

    _____

5. Complete the sentences using the modals from the box.

has to	doesn't have to	had to
have to	don't have to	didn't have to

1. I _____ take a test to enter this English class.
2. The students _____ pay tuition before this class started.
3. The students _____ pay for books.
4. I _____ take this class in the morning. There are evening classes.
5. I _____ do homework every day.
6. The teacher _____ take attendance.
7. The students _____ write compositions or essays.
8. In my country, students _____ wear uniforms.
9. In my country, the teachers _____ give many tests.
10. In my country, I _____ study a few hours every day.
11. In my country, the students _____ study English.

6. Read each situation and give your advice. Explain your reasons. Use *should* or *shouldn't*.

> You **should buy** a present from her list. It will be something that she needs for her new apartment.
> He **shouldn't arrive** late. He will interrupt the ceremony.

1. Paul works at a company where everyone speaks his native language. Paul is taking English classes twice a week, but no one at his job will practice speaking English with him. What should he do?

   <u>He should find a classmate to practice with.</u>

   _____

   _____

2. Julia needs help. Her apartment is always a mess! All of her rooms are piled with boxes, books, and papers. The kitchen table is covered with so many old bills, newspapers, and magazines that she can't use it. What should she do?

   _____

   _____

   _____

3. Adrienne and Kenny are getting married in two months. Almost everything is ready. There's one problem—Adrienne's dog, Muffin. Adrienne wants her dog to be in her wedding ceremony, but Kenny doesn't. The dog is becoming a serious problem. Adrienne says that her dog is like a family member, and she can't imagine the ceremony without Muffin. What should they do?

   _____

   _____

   _____

4. Makiko and Shinjo want to have a small wedding with family and a few close friends. They're afraid that their other friends will be angry. What should they do?

   _____

   _____

   _____

7. Listen and take notes about each family member.

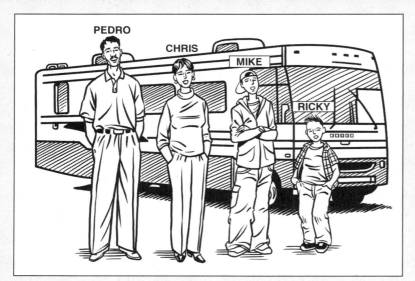

Notes

8. Listen and write the name of each family member. You may also write *No one does* or *Everyone does*.

1. Pedro   4. _____   7. _____

2. _____   5. _____   8. _____

3. _____   6. _____   9. _____

9. Listen and complete the answers to the questions. Use a modal in each answer.

1. They _____ have to stop _____ occasionally because it's a long trip.

2. They _____ a cooler because there's a refrigerator in the RV.

3. They _____ because there are many interesting places to see.

4. He _____ them out because an agency did it for him.

5. She _____ him because he's only seven.

6. They _____ any because they're going to eat out.

7. They _____ more than one so that more than one person can take pictures.

8. They _____ some so that the children won't be bored.

China is a large country and the most populated country in the world. The wedding customs in China vary according to regions. Below is a description of a few typical Chinese wedding customs.

Wedding preparations Traditionally, the groom's family has to pay for the wedding party. They also have to pay for a place for the couple to live. The bride and her family provide the household: kitchen supplies, bed linens, furniture, and today they may even provide the electronic appliances such as a washer and dryer.

Clothes A Chinese bride does not have to wear white. She will often wear red because red is a lucky color in Chinese culture. Today, a modern bride may wear a western-style wedding gown, but she may change into a Chinese-style gown later in the ceremony. The groom usually wears a dark suit.

The ceremony and celebration Chinese wedding ceremonies are simple. First, the couple must go to a local government office to get a marriage certificate. After they fill out the paperwork, an official checks the forms. Then, they are legally married. The bride and groom do not exchange rings, and the new bride does not have to change her name. She can keep her family's name.

The reception takes place in a hotel, a restaurant, or a wedding hall. Before the reception, the groom must pick up the bride at her family's home. At the family home the bride's family may play tricks on the groom before they let him take the bride away. Sometimes the groom gives the family gifts. Then, he will take his bride to the reception in a rented car—often a red one.

Everyone has a good time at the reception. It is a time to celebrate the happiness of the new couple. There is a beautiful banquet with many delicious dishes. A respected older relative will introduce the new couple and make a speech. Then, the couple has to visit each table of guests to receive good wishes from each guest. Many of the guests will stand up in front of all the friends and family and express their good wishes for the couple. After the older relatives and friends leave, the young people take over the party. There is music, singing, and dancing. The friends of the couple organize many games for the guests and for the bride and groom. The friends of the bride may play funny tricks on the groom.

The guests give all kinds of practical gifts for the couple's new home. Gifts of money in special red envelopes are also popular. The mothers of the bride and groom will each make a quilt for the couple's bed. In the corners of the quilt are four items: dates, peanuts, dried beans, and sunflower seeds. They represent the hope that the couple will soon have children, boys and girls.

Read the questions. Then, number and <u>underline</u> the answers in the passage.

1. What are the differences between a Chinese wedding and a wedding in your native country?

2. Why does a Chinese bride wear red?

3. What happens when the older guests leave?

4. What is the meaning of the four items in the corners of the quilts?

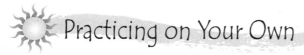

The Greatest and the Smallest

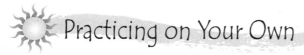

![sun icon] Practicing on Your Own

1. Complete the sentences with the superlative forms of the adjectives in the box. You may use some adjectives more than once.

cheap	easy
elegant	bad
comfortable	difficult
safe	fast
impressive	stylish
economical	popular
good	spacious

1. The minivan is _____the most comfortable_____.

2. The minivan is _____.

3. The minivan is _____.

4. The minivan is _____ for a large family.

5. The sports car is _____.

6. The sports car is _____ in bad weather.

7. The sports car is _____.

8. The sports car is _____ for a very tall person.

9. The subcompact is _____.

10. The subcompact is _____.

11. The subcompact is _____ for a single person.

12. The subcompact is _____ to park.

2. Complete the sentences using *one of the* and the superlative form of the adjectives in parentheses.

> New York City is one of the most exciting cities in the world.

1. Paris, France is ___one of the most beautiful cities___ in the world.
   (beautiful city)

2. The Empire State Building is _____
   in the world.   (tall building)

3. Firefighters have _____.
                              (dangerous job)

4. Tokyo, Japan is _____ in the world.
                          (crowded city)

5. Florida is _____ for retirees.
                      (popular state)

6. The giraffe is _____ in the animal
   kingdom.   (heavy animal)

7. Phoenix, Arizona is _____ in the
   world.   (sunny place)

8. Niagara Falls is _____ for tourists.
                          (popular site)

9. Michael Jordan was _____ in the
   NBA.   (talented basketball player)

10. The Shanghai Public Library is _____ in the
    world.   (large library)

Write five sentences about places in your country. Use *one of the* and a superlative adjective.

11. _____

12. _____

13. _____

14. _____

15. _____

3. Your opinion. Write the brand name of a product and complete the sentences using the superlative form of the adjectives in parentheses.

I think J & C aspirin is *the most effective.*
I think General Store aspirin works *the fastest.*

1. I think _____ sneakers are _____

   _____ (comfortable).

2. I think _____ coffee is _____

   _____ (strong).

3. I think _____ is _____
   (refreshing) in hot weather.

4. I think _____ is _____
   (good) in cold weather.

5. I think _____ are _____
   (juicy).

6. I think _____ is _____
   (satisfying) when I'm very hungry.

4. Complete the sentences with a food or beverage and the superlative form of the adjectives or phrases.

1. I think _____.
   (sweet fruit)

2. I think _____.
   (sour fruit)

3. I think _____.
   (good dessert)

4. I think _____.
   (easy meal to prepare)

5. Contrast. Write one superlative and one comparative sentence about each group.

Dangerous sport	
boxing	1. <u>Boxing is more dangerous than American football.</u>
race car driving	
skiing	2. <u>Skiing is the most dangerous sport of the group.</u>
American football	

Delicious dessert
ice cream
cake
fruit
cookies

3. _____

4. _____

Good World Cup
teams
Brazil
Germany
Argentina
Italy
Peru

5. _____

6. _____

Popular ways to
communicate
telephone
e-mail
cell phone
letters

7. _____

8. _____

6. Edit. Find and correct the adjective mistakes in each sentence.

1. Dogs are ^**the** most popular pets in the United States.

2. Birds are many more popular in China than in the United States.

3. Computer software is the more popular item to buy on the Internet.

4. That Thai restaurant serves the more spicy food in town.

5. Denver International is one of busiest airports in the United States.

6. Soccer is more popular then tennis.

Listening

7. Listen and complete the information about the New York City subway system.

City	Year opened	Number of stations	Number of lines	Number of passengers per day	Cost	Hours open
London Tube	1863	275	12	2,400,000	$2.70–$6.25	5:30 A.M.–11:30 P.M.
Moscow Metro	1935	163	11	9,000,000	$ .14	last train 1:00 A.M.
New York City Subway						

8. Look at the chart. Listen and write the name of the correct subway system.

1. __London Tube__   5. _____

2. _____ 6. _____

3. _____ 7. _____

4. _____ 8. _____

9. Fun facts. Listen and complete the sentences.

1. France has won _____ *the most gold medals* _____ for cycling.

2. Italians drink _____ of bottled water.

3. Walking is _____ in the United States.

4. Americans are _____ consumers of soda.

5. *Spider Man* is _____ movies ever made.

6. India produces _____ any other country.

7. Harvard University is _____ in the United States.

8. The Chicago Public Library is _____ in the United States.

Reading: The State Hermitage Museum

The State Hermitage Museum is one of the most famous art museums in the world. It has one of the largest collections. The Hermitage is located in Saint Petersburg, Russia. In the eighteenth century, it was built as the Winter Palace for Empress Catherine. She collected many works of art. Emperor Nicholas I opened the collection to the public in 1852, and he made the following rules:

1. Everyone had to have a ticket.
2. Visitors had to check their coats, canes, and umbrellas.
3. Visitors were not allowed to touch any of the objects.

His rules were not very different from the rules of today's museums. By 1880 there were already fifty thousand people a year coming to the museum.

There are twelve departments at the Hermitage, including the Department of Western European Art and the Oriental Department. Eighteen hundred full-time employees work at the Hermitage in addition to a large number of volunteers. A large staff is necessary to take care of the present collection of over three million pieces of art.

One of the oldest libraries in Russia is also a part of the Hermitage Museum. The Hermitage has its own research library. It includes books on art, culture, history, and architecture. It also includes the personal collections of Catherine the Great. Visitors from other countries can use the library because many of the materials are available in European and Asian languages.

The Hermitage is open from 10:30 A.M. to 6 P.M. every day except Monday and special holidays. About two million people a year visit the exhibits. Admission is about $.50 for Russian citizens and $10.00 for all others, but many visitors can enter for free, including students, veterans of World War II, families with more than three children, and children under the age of 17.

Scan the reading and complete the chart. How does the Hermitage compare to the other famous art museums?

Museum	Year opened	Number of departments	Visitors per year	Cost for adults	Hours open
Hermitage Museum, St. Petersburg					
Musée du Louvre, Paris	1793	7	5.8 million	$10 (before 3 P.M.) $8.50 (after 3 P.M.)	Mon. & Wed. 9:00 A.M.–9:45 P.M. Thurs.–Sun. 9:00 A.M.–6:00 P.M. Closed Tues.
Metropolitan Museum of Art, New York	1870	13	5.2 million	$12	Sun.–Thurs. 9:30 A.M.–5:30 P.M. Fri.–Sat. 9:30 A.M.–9:00 P.M.

In your notebook, write ten sentences comparing the three museums.

12 Working Parents

Practicing on Your Own

1. Match the two parts of each sentence.

__d__	1. As soon as the phone rings,	**a.** until he finishes his homework.
_____	2. My son can't watch TV	**b.** I drop my son off at school.
_____	3. When my daughter plays soccer,	**c.** he wears a helmet.
_____	4. Before I go to work,	**d.** I answer it.
_____	5. As soon as I get a bill,	**e.** my mother baby-sits.
_____	6. When my son rides his bicycle,	**f.** we watch her game.
_____	7. When Amy gets home from school,	**g.** I read them a story.
_____	8. Before my children go to bed,	**h.** my husband washes the dishes.
_____	9. When we go out at night,	**i.** I pay it.
_____	10. After we have dinner,	**j.** she does her homework.

2. Complete the sentences with information about your schedule.

1. As soon as I get up, _____.
2. I _____ after I eat breakfast.
3. I never _____ before I go to school.
4. Before I leave for school, _____.
5. As soon as I get to school, _____.
6. When my English class is over, _____.
7. _____ after I get home from school.
8. I do my homework when _____.
9. After I do my homework, _____.
10. I eat my dinner when _____.
11. I watch TV until _____.

3. The pictures above describe Amy's day. Read the sentences and (circle) *T* for *True* or *F* for *False*.

1. As soon as she gets up, Amy takes a shower.   T   (F)

2. Amy takes a shower after she comes home from her walk.   T   F

3. Before she goes to work, Amy eats breakfast.   T   F

4. Amy goes to school before she goes to work.   T   F

5. When she gets home from school, Amy eats dinner.   T   F

6. Amy watches TV when she eats dinner.   T   F

7. After work and school, Amy likes to relax.   T   F

8. Amy takes a shower before she goes to bed.   T   F

4. Complete these sentences about Amy's day with *after, before, until,* or *when.*

1. Amy takes a walk _____*after*_____ she gets up.

2. _____ it's raining, Amy doesn't walk.

3. She takes a shower _____ she goes to work.

4. Amy never eats breakfast _____ she goes to work.

5. Amy goes directly to school _____ she finishes work.

6. _____ she gets home, Amy eats dinner.

7. Amy washes the dishes _____ she finishes dinner.

8. _____ Amy goes to bed, she watches TV or reads a book.

9. Amy watches TV _____ she feels tired.

10. _____ Amy is tired, she goes to bed.

5. In each group cross out the adjective with a different meaning.

1. happy   ~~scared~~   pleased

2. angry   mad   tired

3. nervous   calm   worried

4. relaxed   frightened   scared

5. amazed   surprised   exhausted

6. angry   calm   relaxed

7. depressed   puzzled   sad

6. Use the situations in the box below. Describe how you feel about each situation using an adjective from Exercise 5. You can use the same adjective more than once.

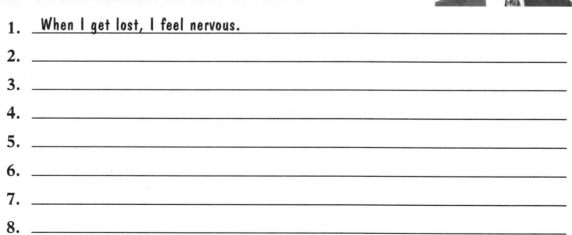

You get lost.
You are stuck in traffic.
You see a large spider.
You are giving a big party.
You have to give a speech.
It rains for a week.
The phone rings in the middle of the night.
You pass a difficult test.
You can't find your keys.
Your child says, "I love you."
You are on vacation.

1. _When I get lost, I feel nervous._____

2. _____

3. _____

4. _____

5. _____

6. _____

7. _____

8. _____

9. _____

10. _____

11. _____

7. Complete. Write the correct pronoun.

1. After my daughter finishes her homework, _____she_____ talks on the phone.

2. When my children come home from school, I'm happy to see _____.

3. When my son finishes school, _____ walks home with his friends.

4. When my children are ready, I walk _____ to school.

5. When my son goes to the park, my husband watches _____.

6. When my daughter has her baby, I'll stay with _____ for two weeks.

7. When I make dinner, the children often help _____.

8. Combine these sentences. Use *before, after,* or *when*. Change the underlined words to pronouns.

1. My son goes to school. I make lunch for <u>my son</u>.
   Before my son goes to school, I make lunch for him.

2. She drops off her daughter at day care. <u>Her daughter</u> cries.
   _____

3. My children come home from school. <u>My children</u> play with their friends.
   _____

4. My son comes home. I help <u>my son</u> with his homework.
   _____

5. My daughter needs a ride. <u>My daughter</u> calls me.
   _____

6. I'm tired. I order take-out food.
   _____

7. My son goes to bed. <u>My son</u> puts out his clothes for the next day.
   _____

8. My daughter goes to sleep. I read <u>my daughter</u> a story.
   _____

9. My children go to bed. <u>My children</u> take their baths.
   _____

10. My children go to bed. I take a long, hot bath.
    _____

Listening

9. Listen to these sentences. Circle the action that happens first.

1. **(a.)** He reads the newspaper. **b.** He eats breakfast.
2. **a.** She eats lunch. **b.** She washes her hands.
3. **a.** I get dressed. **b.** I listen to the weather report.
4. **a.** She takes a walk. **b.** She eats dinner.
5. **a.** He has a cup of coffee. **b.** He eats breakfast.
6. **a.** I get to work. **b.** I call my husband.
7. **a.** I watch TV. **b.** I do my homework.

10. Listen to these young people describe their families' expectations. Then, circle the correct verb in each sentence.

1. I **can /(can't)** dye my hair.

2. In my country, parents **allow / don't allow** girls to go out on dates alone.

3. My parents **let / don't let** me drive the family car.

4. My younger brothers **can / can't** use the Internet when my parents are at work.

5. Children **are supposed to / aren't supposed to** walk to school alone.

6. My parents **let / don't let** my sister talk on the phone at night.

7. Children **are supposed to / aren't supposed to** help their parents at home.

8. I **am allowed to / not allowed to** go to the movies with my friends.

11. Listen to Ella talk about her morning routine. Then, answer the questions.

1. What does Ella do when she wakes up?

   When Ella wakes up, she makes her lunch.

2. Does she take a shower before or after the baby wakes up?

   _____

3. When does she eat?

   _____

4. When does she wake the baby?

   _____

5. When does she give Jesse a bottle?

   _____

6. What does she do after she changes and dresses Jesse?

_____

7. What does Ella do before she leaves her mother's house?

_____

☀ Reading: Day Care Centers

In most communities, there are a large number of child care centers, day care centers, and nursery schools. The programs may be similar or very different in terms of their hours, cost, and the ages of children they accept. How can parents decide which program is best for their child?

It is best to visit three or more programs. Look at the facility and the classrooms carefully. Programs should have safe and clean indoor and outdoor play areas. Be sure that the classrooms are bright and attractive. There should be a variety of educational and fun toys, books, equipment, and games. In many classrooms, games and activities are organized in centers, such as sand or water play areas, arts and crafts areas, reading areas with books and rugs and pillows, an area with blocks and other building materials, and so on.

Ask about the program. Programs for small children should emphasize language skills. There should be songs, stories, games, and the introduction of colors, shapes, and letters. Ask how many teachers and assistants there are in each class. How many children in the program speak your child's language? Do any of the teachers or the assistants speak your child's language? Do you want your child to attend a bilingual program?

It is important that parents be able to visit the program and observe the classes. The children should be interested and happy. They should know the rules and procedures of the class, such as take turns, do not take a toy away from another child, put your toys away after you play, and walk—don't run—in the classroom.

Start to look and plan early for child care. Some popular programs have a waiting list of a year or longer. In some areas, if you qualify because of low income, the government may help you pay for child care.

You are talking to a day care director. Write five questions you want to ask about the program.

1. _____

2. _____

3. _____

4. _____

5. _____

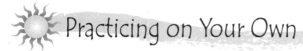

13 Crime

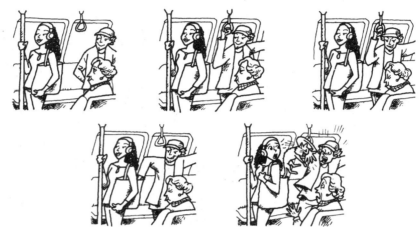

1. **Look at the pictures and complete the sentences with *before, after, when,* or *as soon as.***

   1. _____**After**_____ Jill got on the subway, she grabbed a pole.

   2. Reggie noticed Jill's large open purse _____ she got on the subway.

   3. _____ Reggie did anything, he moved closer to Jill. He noticed that she was wearing headphones.

   4. _____ the older woman next to Reggie fell asleep, he took his opportunity.

   5. Reggie looked around _____ he reached into her bag.

   6. Something bit Reggie _____ he put his hand in Jill's bag. It was her cat!

   7. Jill turned _____ she heard Reggie scream.

2. **Complete the sentences with *before, after, when,* or *as soon as.* For some sentences more than one answer is possible.**

   1. _____ I got up this morning, I checked the weather report.

   2. I listened to the weather report _____ I got dressed.

   3. _____ I got dressed, I had my breakfast.

4. _____ I finished breakfast, I put the dishes in the dishwasher.

5. I brushed my teeth _____ I finished breakfast.

6. I took my keys and my books _____ I left the house.

7. _____ I left the house, I locked the door.

3. **Complete the sentences with the past continuous form of one of the verbs from the box.**

describe	light	look	look
play	read	relax	take
sit	watch		

I He She It	was	watching a movie. walking in the park. driving to work. locking the door.
You We They	were	

1. While the children _____ **were taking** _____ their first roller coaster ride, their mother _____ **was watching** _____ from the ground.

2. My mother and I _____ on the porch while my dad and brother _____ the fire.

3. Yoshiko _____ at a statue while Leo _____ information about the artist.

4. Monica _____ the sights while her friends _____ at everything.

5. While Mr. and Mrs. Walker _____ , their daughter _____ in the sand.

4. Match the time clauses on the left with the main clauses on the right.

> **While** I was reading, I **heard** a noise.
> **When** I heard the noise, I **stopped** reading.

_c_ 1. While John was running
down the hill,

_____ 2. When I turned on the light,

_____ 3. While Joan was riding the bus,

_____ 4. When my car broke down,

_____ 5. While I was reading a book,

_____ 6. While the students were
taking their exam,

_____ 7. When I unlocked the door,

_____ 8. While we were watching the
exciting soccer game on TV,

a. our dinner burned.

b. our dog tried to run out of
the house

c. he tripped and hurt his knee.

d. someone stole her wallet.

e. the phone rang.

f. the lightbulb exploded.

g. I called the automobile
association.

h. one student's cell phone rang.

5. Complete the sentences. Use your imagination.

1. While I was studying, _____.

2. I was watching TV when _____.

3. The students were talking while _____.

4. The teacher was playing a video while the students _____

_____.

5. I _____ while I was exercising.

6. I _____ while I was listening to a CD.

7. When I got up this morning, _____.

8. _____ when the students
entered the classroom.

9. I was doing my homework when _____.

6. Write two sentences about each set of pictures. In one sentence, use a past tense clause with *when,* and in the other, use a past continuous clause with *while.*

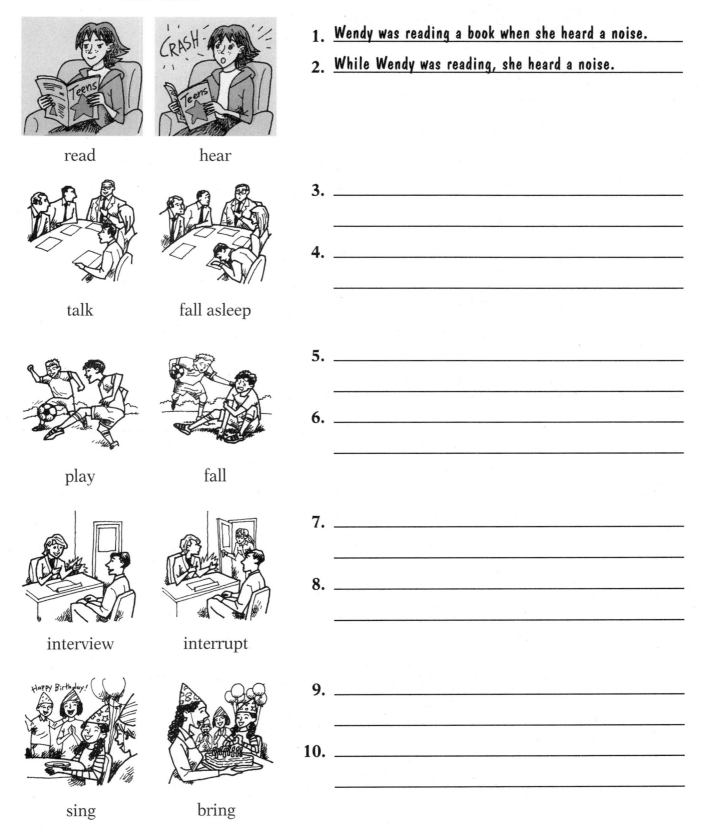

read   hear

1. <u>Wendy was reading a book when she heard a noise.</u>
2. <u>While Wendy was reading, she heard a noise.</u>

talk   fall asleep

3. _____
   _____
4. _____
   _____

play   fall

5. _____
   _____
6. _____
   _____

interview   interrupt

7. _____
   _____
8. _____
   _____

sing   bring

9. _____
   _____
10. _____
   _____

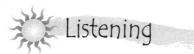 Listening

7. **Dictation.** Listen and complete the sentences.

1. I _____was walking_____ down the street when I
   _____saw_____ a traffic accident.

2. A man _____ into the intersection when a truck
   _____ him off.

3. The man in the car _____ his horn when the truck
   driver suddenly _____.

4. After the truck _____, both drivers
   _____ of their vehicles.

5. While they _____, a taxi suddenly
   _____ the back of the car.

6. The taxi driver _____ attention when he
   _____ the car.

7. Fortunately, a police officer _____ out of a coffee
   shop when the accident _____.

8. **Listen to the 911 phone call. Complete the summary of the phone call with appropriate words. You will have to listen to the conversation more than once.**

Cecilia Roberts _____was coming_____ home from

_____. She _____ into her

_____ when she noticed that the door was

_____. She dialed _____.

The operator _____ her some questions. Cecilia

was calling from her _____. She was parked in the

_____ of her home. Then, the operator asked for Cecilia's

_____. Suddenly the door _____,

and someone began coming out of the _____. At the

same time, the operator was trying to get all of _____'s

information. Then, Cecilia noticed that the person who

_____ out of the house was her _____.

Cecilia apologized to the _____.

78   UNIT 13

One of the responsibilities of American citizens is to serve on a **jury.** A jury is a group of 10 to 12 citizens who listen to the evidence in a trial. A jury's task is to decide if the **defendant,** the person who is on trial, is guilty or not guilty. Jury members have to serve for one to two days to many weeks depending on the type of trial. In some states, **jurors** have to report for only one or two days. Here is an example of a typical juror's day.

Dan Wilson received a **jury duty notice** in the mail. He told his employer and two weeks later, he reported to the courthouse. Dan had to report to the courthouse by 8:00 A.M. and receive his name badge. Before he and the **jurors** went into the courtroom, they watched a video about jury service. There were 50 other **jurors** that day, so Dan had to wait a long time before they called his number. The **defense attorney,** the lawyer representing the man on trial, selected Dan for the jury. Not all of the people who were called to **jury** duty were selected for a trial, so some people could go home.

The trial was scheduled for the next day, so Dan was permitted to go home. Before he entered the courthouse the next morning, he turned off his cell phone and put on his jury badge. At 8:30, the jurors went into the courtroom.

Before the trial began, the jurors had to **swear,** or promise, to make their decision according to the law and the **evidence** or facts. After both lawyers presented their cases, the judge delivered instructions to the jury.

The jury went into the jury room to **deliberate,** or discuss the trial. The jurors elected one person to be the **foreman** of the jury. The foreperson led the discussion. After the jurors reached a **verdict,** the foreperson read it to the judge in the courtroom. In the trial that Dan participated in, the **verdict** was "Not guilty."

Read the passage and match the vocabulary words and phrases on the left with the phrases on the right.

__f__ **1.** A jury

_____ **2.** A defendant

_____ **3.** A juror

_____ **4.** A jury duty notice

_____ **5.** The evidence

_____ **6.** The jurors had to swear

_____ **7.** The jurors deliberated

_____ **8.** The foreman

_____ **9.** A verdict

_____ **10.** The defense attorney

a. is the facts of the trial.

b. to listen to all of the evidence at a trial.

c. is a final decision.

d. in order to reach a decision after all the facts were presented.

e. represents a defendant in a trial.

f. consists of a group of 10 or 12 American citizens.

g. leads the jury discussion about the trial.

h. is one member of the jury.

i. is accused of a crime.

j. is a written request for jury service.

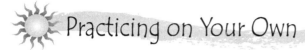

14 Careers

Practicing on Your Own

> **Future Time Clauses**
> If I *lose* my job, I *will look* for another one.
> Before I *look* for another job, I *will revise* my résumé.
> I *will buy* a new car when I *get* a promotion.
> I'*m going to be* happier after I *start* my new job.

1. Complete the sentences with *before, when, after,* or *if.*

1. I will get a job _____after_____ I graduate.

2. I won't get a full-time job _____ I go to school full-time.

3. _____ I finish my classes, I will go straight home.

4. _____ I get stuck in traffic, I will be late for work.

5. _____ I finish the nursing program, I will have to take an important state exam.

6. My supervisor will be angry _____ I make another mistake.

7. I'm going to buy a new suit _____ I go to my interview.

8. _____ I get home from the interview, I'm going to call my best friend.

2. Match the time clause on the left with the appropriate main clause on the right.

___f___ 1. If I do well in my biology course,

_____ 2. After Andrea finishes her courses,

_____ 3. Before Steven leaves for his trip,

_____ 4. After the mall opens,

_____ 5. If the company lays me off,

_____ 6. Before the employees receive a raise,

_____ 7. When the company moves,

_____ 8. If the company expands,

a. I'll have to look for another job.

b. they will have evaluations.

c. many people will lose their jobs.

d. his secretary will confirm his flight.

e. it will need more workers.

f. I'll take a chemistry course.

g. many stores will need salespeople.

h. she will have an associate's degree.

3. Emily received a promotion and a raise yesterday. What is she going to do? Look at the pictures and write sentences about the possibilities. Use *may* or *might* and words from the box.

> *May* and *Might* express possibility.
> I **might take** a vacation in January.   She **might ask** for a promotion.
> I **may stay** for three weeks.   She **may get** the promotion if she asks.

buy
celebrate
e-mail
get
go out
move
save
take

1.
2.
3.
4.
5.
6.
7.

1. Emily __might celebrate with her friends__.
2. She _____.
3. She _____.
4. _____
5. _____
6. _____
7. _____

4. Read each situation. Answer the question using *may* or *might*.

1. Alex quit his job as an accountant because his dream is to be a musician. What are his parents going to do?
   __They might tell him to go back to his job.__

   What are his friends going to do?

   _____

2. Anne is very good with animals, and she gets good grades in biology class. What are her career plans? Write two possibilities.

   _____
   _____

5. Look at each picture. Complete each main clause. Use the future tense or *may* or *might*. There is more than one possible correct answer.

1. When her husband comes home, she <u>might take a</u> <u>long hot bath to relax</u>.

2. If her husband doesn't come home on time, she _____.

3. If their neighbors turn down the music, _____.

4. If their neighbors don't turn down the music, _____ _____.

5. When the dog's owners come home, _____.

6. If they don't come home soon, _____.

7. If the driver has an accident, _____.

8. If a police officer sees them, _____.

9. If Mr. Kim passes the eye test, _____.

10. If he doesn't pass the eye test, _____.

11. If Ruth feels better, she _____.

12. If she doesn't feel better soon, _____.

6. Combining sentences. Read the pairs of sentences. Combine each pair into a sentence with a future time clause. Remember to place the comma in the correct place. Change repeated subjects to pronouns.

1. if / it / rain   we / come home / early
   If it rains, we will come home early.

2. before / I / start work   I / check / messages
   _____

3. I / buy / new car   when / I / get / new job
   _____

4. if / Bob and Jane / have time   Bob and Jan / go / to the movies
   _____

5. Before / John / go to his interview   John / research / the company
   _____

6. Sophia / go back / to college   if / Sophia / lose her job
   _____

7. if / Rick / get a promotion   Rick / be / very pleased
   _____

8. Mara / give away / her winter clothes   Maria / move to Florida
   _____

7. Edit. Find and correct the mistakes. There is one verb mistake in each sentence.

                                   will take
1. After Jackie talks to her supervisor, she ~~take~~ a few days off.

2. If Jackie's boss won't give her time off, she will have a problem.

3. When Pierre gets home from work, he always went for a long run in the park.

4. He takes a long shower before he is eating dinner.

5. While Beata was look for her keys, her son found them in the car.

6. Beata called her husband after she was finding her keys.

7. Before Herman went to a job counselor, he reads the classified ads.

8. If he won't get a job today, he will take a job with his uncle.

 Listening

8. Listen to Mr. Miller's job interview. Then, read the questions and (circle) the answers.

1. What did Mr. Miller major in?

   (a.) computer programming

   b. computer repairs

   c. computer education

2. How long did he work at his other job?

   a. twenty years   b. two years   c. two months

3. Why did he leave that job?

   a. He was laid off.   b. He was fired.   c. He quit.

4. Why doesn't he have a job in computer programming?

   a. He doesn't like computers.

   b. The salaries are high.

   c. The economy is slow.

5. What will he do at the new job? (Circle) all correct answers.

   a. He will repair computers.   c. He will teach computer classes.

   b. He will sell computers.   d. He will answer questions at a help desk.

6. If his sales are good, he will . . .

   a. earn $50 an hour.

   b. earn a 10% commission.

   c. earn more money after six months.

7. Mr. Miller will receive a phone call . . .

   a. if he likes the job.   b. if he gets the job.   c. if a class is available.

9. Listen and (circle) each correct main clause.

1. (a.) I locked it.   b. I opened it.
2. a. she writes it.   b. she'll go to the bank.
3. a. he leaves work.   b. he will help his kids with their homework.
4. a. Mia will relax.   b. Mia asked questions.
5. a. she will arrive at the office.   b. she put on her uniform.
6. a. he'll take a sick day from work.   b. he'll get sick.

When the economy is slow and people lose their jobs, they begin looking at different careers. They consider careers that they did not think about before. Today, there are more men training to work in fields that used to be popular only with women. One of those fields is nursing. Today, there are more men working as registered nurses than ever before.

First, the nursing profession has a very strong future. According to the U.S. Department of Labor, by 2010, there will be 32% more job openings for registered nurses. Some nursing students may have job offers before they graduate from nursing school.

Second, salaries are good. A new nurse may start at $39,700. An experienced nurse may earn as much as $90,000 a year in addition to receiving excellent benefits. So, why shouldn't a man want to become a nurse?

The number of registered nurses increased from 57,000 in 1983 to 164,000 in 2002. However, this does not mean that it is easy for men to be in a traditionally female profession. Some men experience discrimination from patients. Friends and family might think that being a nurse is a "woman's job." Men who cannot handle the criticism may decide early on to drop out of nursing school. Or, men who make it through nursing school might quit later on because of the pressure.

Besides the salaries, men may choose to become nurses because they want a more meaningful or satisfying career. Other professions may pay much higher salaries, but they may not give as much satisfaction as nursing does. So, in the future, don't be surprised if the nurse who comes into your hospital room is named Bob.

Understanding statistics and facts. Read the passage and answer the questions. Circle *T* for *True* or *F* for *False*.

1. There are more male nurses than there used to be.   (T)   F

2. There will be twice as many jobs for nurses in 2010.   T   F

3. An experienced nurse may earn more than $90,000 a year.   T   F

4. There were more than twice as many nurses in 2002 than there were in 1983.   T   F

5. All male nurses experience discrimination.   T   F

6. Some families find it difficult to accept the idea of a male nurse.   T   F

7. Nursing is a meaningful career.   T   F

15 | City Life

Practicing on Your Own

1. Complete these sentences with *for* or *since*.

1. She's been walking in the park ____for____ an hour.
2. He's been talking to his coworker _____ 20 minutes.
3. They've been waiting for the bus _____ 8:00.
4. He's been driving people around town _____ 7:00.
5. She's been talking on her cell phone _____ two hours.
6. She's been working on her computer _____ she got to work.
7. He's been taking a break _____ 25 minutes.
8. She's been looking for a job _____ a long time.
9. He's been delivering mail _____ 9:00.
10. They've been working for the fire department _____ 1995.

2. Write in the present perfect continuous. Use *for* or *since*.

1. Victor arrived at the train station 30 minutes ago. (wait)

   Victor has been waiting for the train for 30 minutes.

2. Carlos moved to Canada in 2000. (live)

   _____

3. Debbie arrived at school an hour ago. (sit in class)

   _____

4. Eva sat down at a library table at 10:00 this morning. (study)

   _____

5. Maria is driving across the country. She left on Saturday. (drive)

   _____

6. Jose and Elena met at a party three months ago. (date)

   _____

7. Ali turned on the TV four hours ago. (watch)

   _____

3. Answer the questions about each occupation.

1. What's he doing?

   <u>He's bringing an order to a table.</u>

2. How long has he been serving tables?

   <u>He's been serving tables since 5:00.</u>

3. What's she doing?

   _____

4. How long has she been standing on her feet?

   _____

5. What's she doing?

   _____

6. How long has she been selling flowers?

   _____

7. What's he doing?

   _____

8. How long has he been watching the shoppers?

   _____

9. What's she doing?

   _____

10. How long has she been taking photographs?

   _____

4. **Tense contrast.** Answer the questions about the picture. Use your imagination!

1. What is Officer Ortiz doing?
   <u>He is writing a ticket.</u>

2. Where was Mrs. Lee?

   _____

3. How much is the fine for parking overtime?

   _____

4. What is Officer Ortiz going to do next?

   _____

5. How long have Mr. Thomas and Peter been arguing?

   _____

6. Whose fault was the accident?

   _____

7. What is Elena looking at?

_____

8. How long has she been sitting in the park?

_____

9. Does she know Michael and Luisa?

_____

10. How long have the children been playing in the park?

_____

11. What is Jane doing?

_____

12. What did she order?

_____

13. How long has she been sitting at that table?

_____

14. Is Joseph going to start a conversation with Jane?

_____

 Listening

5. Listen and (circle) the correct answers about the picture on page 88.

1. **a.** Yes, she is.   **b.** Yes, she does.   **c.** Yes, she did.   **(d.)** Yes, she has.

2. **a.** Yes, she is.   **b.** Yes, she does.   **c.** Yes, she did.   **d.** Yes, she has.

3. **a.** Yes, she is.   **b.** Yes, she does.   **c.** Yes, she did.   **d.** Yes, she has.

4. **a.** Yes, he is.   **b.** Yes, he does.   **c.** Yes, he did.   **d.** Yes, he has.

5. **a.** Yes, he is.   **b.** Yes, he does.   **c.** Yes, he did.   **d.** Yes, he has.

6. **a.** Yes, he is.   **b.** Yes, he does.   **c.** Yes, he did.   **d.** Yes, he has.

7. **a.** Yes, he is.   **b.** Yes, he does.   **c.** Yes, he did.   **d.** Yes, he has.

8. **a.** Yes, he is.   **b.** Yes, he does.   **c.** Yes, he did.   **d.** Yes, he has.

9. **a.** Yes, he is.   **b.** Yes, he does.   **c.** Yes, he did.   **d.** Yes, he has.

10. **a.** Yes, he is.   **b.** Yes, he does.   **c.** Yes, he did.   **d.** Yes, he has.

6. Listen and (circle) the sentence with the same meaning.

1. **a.** She worked as a waitress for two years.
   b. She's been working as a waitress for two years.

2. **a.** He worked for five hours.
   b. He has been working for five hours.

3. **a.** Gloria waited for the train for an hour.
   b. Gloria has been waiting for the train for an hour.

4. **a.** Carla jogged in the park for 30 minutes.
   b. Carla has been jogging in the park for 30 minutes.

5. **a.** Thomas tried on many suits.
   b. Thomas has been trying on suits.

6. **a.** Bob cut hair all day.
   b. Bob has been cutting hair all day.

7. **a.** Tuan delivered mail for 25 years.
   b. Tuan has been delivering mail for 25 years.

8. **a.** Lin worked at her computer for six hours.
   b. Lin has been working on her computer for six hours.

7. Listen to the conversations. (Circle) T for *True* or F for *False*.

Conversation 1

1.	George has a job.	T	(F)
2.	George has been looking for a job.	T	F
3.	George applied for a job as a taxi driver.	T	F
4.	George might apply for a job as a taxi driver.	T	F

Conversation 2

5.	Bill is probably a doctor.	T	F
6.	Bill arrived at work ten minutes ago.	T	F
7.	Bill has been sitting in traffic.	T	F
8.	There are two patients in the waiting room.	T	F

Conversation 3

9.	Vera used to date Paul.	T	F
10.	Vera has been going out with Joseph since last month.	T	F
11.	Joseph lives in her apartment building.	T	F
12.	Vera met Joseph at a party at her friend's house.	T	F

Oregon is located in the northwestern part of the United States. Portland is the largest city in the state, with a population of over 500,000. Portland is the fourth largest seaport in the West. The city **sits** on the Williamette River, which **flows** into the Columbia River, then into the Pacific Ocean.

Portland's weather is mild year round. From May to October, the weather is often sunny with light winds. But from November to April, the weather is **wet.** There is usually rain and fog. Portland has 150 days of rain a year! When it isn't raining, residents can see Mt. Hood in the distance. Mt. Hood is the state's tallest mountain at 11,239 feet (3,426 m).

Portland is America's most livable large city. It's a beautiful city with over 160 parks. McCall Waterfront Park runs for 20 blocks along the river. Washington Park is the home of the Rose Tea Garden with over 10,000 rose bushes of 400 different **varieties.** Portland is called the City of Roses. There is a Rose **Festival** every June with hundreds of flower **displays** and a beautiful parade. All the police cars in Portland have pictures of roses on their doors. Washington Park also has a large Japanese garden and a zoo with a **collection** of Asian elephants.

Visitors enjoy Portland's museums. The Portland Art Museum has a large collection of Indian art. The Oregon Historical Society Museum tells the story of the state's history. Families visit the Oregon Museum of Science and History to see the electronics displays, the space station, and the planetarium. Other cultural activities include the Oregon Symphony, an opera company, and many jazz clubs. For lunch and dinner, there are over 1,200 restaurants to choose from. Chinese, Vietnamese, and Japanese restaurants are very popular.

Portland residents enjoy outdoor activities, with biking, hiking, skiing, and water sports in and near the city. It is **rated** as America's number one city for bicyclists, with over 200 miles (322 km) of bike paths. Bike Central in downtown Portland **offers** bike racks and showers for people who want to **commute** by bicycle.

Find a word in bold print with a similar meaning to each word below.

1. graded ___rated___

2. kinds _____

3. rainy _____

4. celebration _____

5. group _____

6. runs _____

7. travel to work _____

8. exhibits _____

9. is located _____

10. provides _____

Audio Script

Unit 1: The First Week
Page 6—Track 1
7. Listen and complete this school diagram.
There aren't any classrooms on the first floor. When you walk into the building, you'll see the security desk on the right, next to the front door. The elevators are next to the front door, on the left. There are two elevators. The stairs are across from the elevators. The rest rooms are across from the front door. The men's room is on the left and the women's room is on the right. Walk into the building. Turn left. The bookstore is at the end of the hall. There is a copy machine in the bookstore. The counselor's office is in Room 105. The nurse's office is across from the counselor's office. When you walk into the building, turn right. The student lounge is at the end of the hall. The ATM machine is in the student lounge. When you walk into the student lounge, turn left. You'll see the ATM machine in the corner. There are five vending machines on the wall to the right. You can buy soda or candy or chips during the break.

Page 6—Track 2
8. Listen and copy only the true sentences about your school.
1. Our teacher is from the United States. **2.** The school gives us our books. **3.** Our class begins at 7:00 P.M. **4.** All of the students in my class speak Spanish. **5.** We have a lot of homework. **6.** We have a break. **7.** I can bring food to class. **8.** My school has a computer lab. **9.** Our break is at 10:30. **10.** We can only speak English in class. **11.** Everyone needs an English dictionary. **12.** There is a test every week.

Page 6—Track 3
9. Listen and circle the letter of the correct response.
1. Where is your office? **2.** What's your e-mail address? **3.** How do I get a library card? **4.** Is there a computer lab in this building? **5.** Can I answer my cell phone during class? **6.** When is the assignment due? **7.** Where is the bookstore? **8.** What are the library hours? **9.** Do we have any vacation days? **10.** When is the first test? **11.** What is the last day of class? **12.** Do we have a final exam in this class? **13.** How many levels are there in this program? **14.** What should I do if I am absent?

Unit 2: The Average American
Page 12—Track 4
8. Listen to David, a teenager, talk about his eating habits. Then, answer the questions.
Adult: So, tell me. What are your eating habits?
David: What do you mean?
Adult: Tell me what you eat. For example, what do you eat for breakfast?
David: I don't eat breakfast every day. I get up too late.
Adult: Don't your parents prepare breakfast for you?
David: They're busy, too, but sometimes my mother gives me a piece of fruit or a breakfast bar to eat on the way to the bus.
Adult: How about lunch? Do you always eat lunch?
David: Yes, I do.
Adult: Do you take your lunch to school?
David: Yeah, I usually do.
Adult: What do you eat?
David: I eat a sandwich, a piece of fruit, and I drink milk.
Adult: Do you sometimes eat out at lunchtime? Like at a fast-food restaurant or pizzeria?
David: No, I never eat out. I'm only a sophomore. Only seniors can eat out at lunchtime.
Adult: How about dinners? Does your family eat together?
David: Yes, my mother wants us to eat together as often as possible.
Adult: How often does your family eat out?
David: We eat out once a week; we usually have pizza or Chinese food.

Adult: Thank you for answering our survey, David.
David: You're welcome.

Page 12—Track 5
9. Listen and write the sentences.
1. Teenage boys often like to eat out. **2.** The average American eats salads, burgers, and french fries at restaurants. **3.** Most Americans do not carpool to work. **4.** Most American workers do not take public transportation. **5.** Most Americans commute to work alone. **6.** The average commuter spends 26 minutes to get to work. **7.** The average American family owns one or two cars. **8.** The average American family has fewer than four children.

Unit 3: Pets
Page 18—Track 6
7. Listen and circle the correct answers.
1. What kind of dog is that? **2.** What's his name? **3.** He's very big. How much does he weigh? **4.** Does he have his rabies immunization? **5.** Is he good with children? **6.** Is he housebroken? **7.** How old is he? **8.** Who feeds him? **9.** Do you have a dog license? **10.** Does he bark a lot?

Page 18—Track 7
8. Lauri is a dog walker. Read the answers. Then, listen and write the question next to the correct answer.
1. How long do you walk the dogs? **2.** How many customers do you have? **3.** Are you tired at the end of the day? **4.** What do you do? **5.** How often do you walk the dogs? **6.** How much do you charge? **7.** How many dogs do you walk at one time? **8.** Where do you walk the dogs?

Page 18—Track 8
9. First, listen to the information about Chihuahuas. Then, circle T for True of F for False.
Chihuahuas are one of the smallest dogs. They are only about six to nine inches tall and they weigh two to six pounds. The ears on a Chihuahua stand straight up. The Chihuahua has a short, curved tail. Chihuahuas are noisy. They like to bark. They are affectionate animals, but they usually like just one or two people. They are nervous dogs and are not the best dog for a home with small children. Chihuahuas are more comfortable in warm weather. They do not like the cold.

Unit 4: The States
Page 24—Track 9
7. First, look at the map. Then, listen and complete the information about Florida.
Florida is located in the southeastern corner of the United States. Florida is a peninsula. That means it is surrounded by water on three sides. The Atlantic Ocean is on the east. The Gulf of Mexico is on the west. At the bottom of Florida is a group of very small islands called the Florida Keys. Key West, on the Florida Keys, is the most southern city in the United States. Florida is a low, flat state with many rivers, lakes, and swamps. There are no mountains in Florida.
Tallahassee is the capital of Florida, but the largest city is Jacksonville. Much of the population of Florida lives in large cities on the coast, such as Miami and Tampa. The population of Florida is about 16 million and growing. In population, it is the fourth most populated state in the nation. Seventeen percent of the population is Hispanic and fifteen percent is African-American. The fastest growing population is senior citizens. Eighteen percent of the population, that is almost 2.8 million people, is 65 years of age or older.
Many people move to Florida to enjoy the beautiful weather. Florida is called the Sunshine State. The weather in the summer is hot and humid, with an average temperature of 81° in July. In January, the coldest month, the average temperature is 60°. Florida receives a lot of rain with an average rainfall of 54 inches.
Florida's economy is strong. Many people work for resorts, restaurants, banks, hotels, and stores.

Florida's farmers grow most of the nation's oranges. Other important crops are tomatoes, sugarcane, and cotton. Tourism is Florida's largest industry. Favorite attractions include Disney World, SeaWorld and Miami Beach.

Page 24—Track 10
8. Listen and circle the correct answers.
1. Where is Florida located? **2.** What islands are at the bottom of Florida? **3.** What is the largest city in Florida? **4.** What is the population of Florida? **5.** What percentage of the population is Hispanic? **6.** What is the fastest growing population in Florida? **7.** What is Florida called? **8.** How much rain does Florida receive? **9.** What is the average temperature in January? **10.** What is Florida's number one crop? **11.** What is Florida's largest industry?

Page 25—Track 11
9. Listen to the questions and write the correct short answers about Florida.
1. Is Florida on the Pacific Ocean? **2.** Are there any mountains in Florida? **3.** Is Miami in the southern part of Florida? **4.** Is Jacksonville the capital of Florida? **5.** Are there many African-Americans in Florida? **6.** Is the number of senior citizens growing? **7.** Is Florida cold in the winter? **8.** Is there a lot of rain in Florida? **9.** Is there any snow in Florida in the winter? **10.** Is farming an important industry?

Unit 5: Computers and the Internet
Page 30
7. Listen and circle the correct answers.

Conversation 1–Track 12
Man: Excuse me. Can you help me?
Woman: Yes, how can I help you?
Man: I'm trying to find information about the United States presidents.
Woman: Are you looking for information about a particular president?
Man: Yes, I am, but I don't know which one yet. I have a homework assignment. I have to do a report on one president.
Woman: Well, you can look on the computers over here and you'll see the books that we have. Or, you can try looking at the whitehouse.gov Web site on the other computers over there.
Man: Thanks a lot.
Woman: You're welcome.

Conversation 2–Track 13
Man: Excuse me. What's that?
Woman: It's a hand-held computer.
Man: A hand-held computer?
Woman: Uh-huh. Some people call them PDAs.
Man: What are you doing now?
Woman: I'm checking my e-mail.
Man: You can do that here?
Woman: Sure. I can use this almost anywhere. See? I'm getting a new message now.
Man: That's cool. Oh, I have to go. They're calling my flight now. Bye.

Page 30—Track 14
8. Look at the picture. Listen and answer the questions.
1. How many people are waiting to order coffee? **2.** What is Jasmine doing? **3.** What is Sam doing? **4.** Is he using a computer? **5.** Are the women next to Sam paying attention to him? **6.** Who is helping people on the computers? **7.** Who is he helping? **8.** Is anyone waiting for a computer?

Unit 6: A Healthy Lifestyle
Page 36—Track 15
9. You will hear nine sentences. Write each sentence next to the picture it refers to.
1. The doctor is taking the man's blood pressure. **2.** This child is receiving an immunization. **3.** This person is having difficulty reading the eye chart. **4.** This person has high blood pressure. **5.** The child

is going to cry.   6. The doctor is going to check his cholesterol.   7. This person needs reading glasses.   8. The doctor is going to write a prescription for glasses.   9. The boy's parents are going to buy him some ice cream.

Page 36
10. Listen to each conversation. Then, answer the questions.

Conversation 1–Track 16
A: By looking at the test results on your arm, we can tell what you are allergic to.
B: I think I'm allergic to cats.
A: Definitely. You're allergic to both cats and dogs.
B: What else?
A: Well, you're allergic to dust and ragweed.
B: Any foods?
A: Just strawberries. None of these reactions are strong, except for animals. Do you have any pets?
B: No, but my children want a dog.
A: I don't recommend that. I can give you a prescription to take now because ragweed is a problem in late summer. And don't eat any strawberries.

Conversation 2–Track 17
A: Mr. Jackson, your blood pressure is very high—140 over 90. You're going to need medication to lower that.
B: I'm not surprised. My mother and father both had high blood pressure.
A: Your cholesterol is too high, also. It's 275. At your age, it shouldn't be over 200.
B: I don't watch my diet very carefully.
A: I'd like you to have a stress test, too. You're only 37 and these test results are troubling. Do you do any exercise, Mr. Jackson?
B: I don't have any time to exercise. I work 10 hours a day.
A: I'm afraid that's one of the reasons for these high numbers. I'm going to give you a prescription for your blood pressure. I'm also going to put you on a low-fat diet to help you lower your cholesterol. Talk to the nurse at the front desk and she'll help you schedule a time for the stress test.

Page 37–Track 18
11. Listen and write short answers about your lifestyle.
1. Are you going to see the dentist this month?
2. Do you exercise two or more times a week?   3. Are you going to take a walk today?   4. Do you eat a lot of fruit?   5. Do you eat breakfast?   6. Are you going to eat dinner today?   7. Do you drink a lot of coffee?   8. Are you going to sleep eight hours tonight?   9. Are you going to relax later?   10. Are you a healthy person?

Unit 7: People and Places
Page 42–Track 19
6. Read the chart about two cities—Cleveland, Ohio and New Orleans, Louisiana. Then, listen and circle the correct answers.
1. This city is much warmer.   2. This city is much colder.   3. There is much more snow in this city.   4. It rains more often in this city.   5. There are many more family restaurants in this city.   6. There are fewer professional sports teams in this city.   7. There are fewer symphonies in this city.   8. There are more art museums in this city.

Page 42–Track 20
7. Listen to the conversations.
Conversation 1: Complete the sentences.
Maggie: *The Matrix* was a great movie, wasn't it?
John: Are you kidding? *Star Wars* was much better.
Maggie: No way, John. *The Matrix* was much more interesting.
John: It was interesting, Maggie, but it wasn't as exciting as *Star Wars*.
Maggie: Oh, it was much more exciting, and the acting was much better. But, *Star Wars* had more spectacular special effects.
John: So, you agree with me. *Star Wars* was better than *The Matrix*.
Maggie: You didn't hear anything I said!

Conversation 2: Circle the adjectives that describe the mother's soup. –Track 21
Al: Mmm. This soup is delicious, Valerie.
Valerie: Thanks, Al. It's your mother's recipe.

Al: It is? It doesn't taste as salty as my mother's.
Valerie: It's not. I used less salt.
Al: It's not as thin as my mother's. My mother's was like water.
Valerie: It's not, Al. It's thicker. I added some cream.
Al: It's not as spicy as my mother's, and it's much tastier.
Valerie: That's right. I added less pepper.
Al: Are you sure that this is my mother's recipe? I hated her soup. This soup is great!
Valerie: I'm glad you like it.

Unit 8: Moving
Page 48–Track 22
8. Listen and complete these answers with a verb in the past tense.
1. When did she come to the United States?   2. How much money did he bring?   3. Where did you find an apartment?   4. Who met her at the airport?   5. Where did he get a job?   6. Who did he live with?   7. When did he apply for a visa?   8. When did he receive his visa?   9. Was he homesick at first?   10. Did you speak any English when you came here?   11. Where did you study?   12. How long did you take English classes?   13. Did you have a driver's license when you came to this country?   14. When did you get your license?   15. Who taught you how to drive?   16. How much did she pay for her car?

Page 48–Track 23
9. Listen to this conversation. Read the questions and check the correct answer. It is possible to check both.
Maria: David, when did you come to the United States?
David: I came here in 1999.
Maria: Me, too. I arrived in 1999.
David: I remember my first year here. It was terrible.
Maria: Terrible? How come?
David: It wasn't what I expected. First, I thought I knew English. I had studied some English in my country, so I thought I would be able to speak.
Maria: And could you?
David: Not at all! I didn't understand anyone. Everybody spoke so fast. And I realized I only knew beginning English. So, I studied English for two years all day and then I worked in a parking lot at night.
Maria: Did you have family here?
David: Just a friend. I lived with him for a month. Then, I found a room to rent.
Maria: How about this job? You're a great hairstylist.
David: That was another problem. I was already a hairstylist in my country. But here, I needed a license. So, after I finished my English classes, I had to go back to school and get my hairstyling license. That took another two years. I worked at that parking lot for four years! How about you?
Maria: My experience was really different. My sister and her husband were here already. My sister just had her second child. She wanted to go back to work and I volunteered to take care of the kids. I went to school at night and studied English.
David: How long did you study English?
Maria: For a long time—four years!
David: Aren't you still at school now?
Maria: Yes, I'm studying to be a dental hygienist.
David: Good luck with school.
Maria: David, my hair looks great! Thanks!

Page 48–Track 24
10. Listen to the conversation. Then, answer each question in a complete sentence.
A: My brother and his wife moved last weekend.
B: Your older brother, Bill?
A: Yeah, Bill and his wife, Susan.
B: Where did they move to?
A: They moved to Denver, Colorado.
B: Why did they move?
A: My brother's company transferred him there.
B: Did he want to move?
A: No, he didn't want to move. He liked the Washington, D.C. area a lot. But his wife was very happy about the move.
B: How come?
A: Because Denver is in the mountains and she loves to ski.
B: Are you going to visit them?
A: Yes. I'm going to visit them this winter. I like to ski, too.

Unit 9: Natural Disasters
Page 54–Track 25
8. You will hear eight questions about a storm. Write each question next to the correct response.
How many workers were out? Were you late for work? What time did the storm begin? Were a lot of trees down? Was your company closed? How long did it take you to get to work? Did the roads flood? What did your supervisor say?

Page 54–Track 26
9. Listen to these instructions given during a heat wave or a drought. Circle the sentence with the same meaning.
1. Wear light clothing.   2. Don't water your lawns.   3. Don't exercise outdoors.   4. Only use a commercial car wash.   5. Drink a lot of water.   6. Use your air conditioner.   7. Take short showers.

Page 54–Track 27
10. Listen and write the short answers.
1. Do you have smoke alarms in your home?   2. Did you call 9-1-1?   3. Were you at home when the earthquake occurred?   4. Did you see the fire?   5. Are you going to prepare a first-aid kit?   6. Do you know how to respond in an emergency?   7. Are you listening to the weather channel?   8. Can you do CPR?   9. Were you ready for the hurricane?   10. Will you help me?   11. Can you stay at my house for the week?   12. Are you going to evacuate?

Unit 10: Wedding Plans
Page 60–Track 28
7. Listen and take notes about each family member.

Pedro and Chris are planning a cross-country trip with their two sons. They're going to drive from their home in Philadelphia, Pennsylvania to Reno, Nevada to spend a week with Pedro's parents. Everyone has a different responsibility for the trip.

Pedro is in charge of the RV. He has to take it to the mechanic. The mechanic has to make sure that the RV is ready for a long trip. Pedro's also in charge of getting maps, gas and directions. He doesn't have to write out the directions because a travel agent is going to do it for him.

Chris is in charge of food. They plan to stop along the way for dinner, but they're going to eat breakfast and lunch on the road. Chris has to buy bread, milk, fruit, lettuce, and meat for sandwiches. She has to buy food for two days. After two days, they will stop and buy more food in the RV, but it's small. There's a refrigerator in the RV, but it's small.

Mike is in charge of cameras and film. He has to check the video camera and the battery. He has to buy film for the cameras, and check the battery of the digital camera. He should test all the cameras before they leave home.

Ricky is in charge of entertainment. It's going to be a long trip, so they have to pack the RV with travel games and DVDs. There's a DVD and a small TV in the back of the RV.

Finally, everyone has to pack. Chris will help Ricky pack because he's only seven. The family is very excited about the trip.

Page 60–Track 29
8. Listen and write the name of each family member. You may also write *No one does* or *Everyone does*.
1. Who has to put gas in the car?   2. Who has to get DVDs?   3. Who has to buy film?   4. Who has to buy food for dinner?   5. Who has to pack?   6. Who has to select games?   7. Who has to pack the maps?   8. Who has to help Ricky?   9. Who has to prepare for the trip?

Page 60–Track 30
9. Listen and complete the answers to the questions. Use a modal in each answer.
1. Why do they have to stop occasionally?   2. Why don't they have to buy a cooler?   3. Why should they stop to visit sights?   4. Why didn't Pedro have to write out directions?   5. Why does Chris have to help Ricky pack?   6. Why don't they have to buy food for dinner?   7. Why should they pack more than one camera?   8. Why should they take games and DVDs?

Unit 11: The Greatest and the Smallest

Page 66–Track 31

7. Listen and complete the information about the New York City subway system.

Public transportation is a necessary part of life in many large cities. New York City has one of the oldest subway systems in the world. New York opened its subway system in 1904. It's a very large system with over 468 stations. The busiest station is the Times Square station, where there are a number of businesses, theaters, hotels, and restaurants. The subway system covers many miles and has 25 different subway lines. Those lines service approximately 3,500,000 riders a day from the north in the Bronx, to the east in Far Rockaway. In 2003, the cost of a single ride increased from $1.50 to $2.00. There's a saying that New York is the city that never sleeps. The subway never sleeps either. It's open 24 hours a day.

Page 66–Track 32

8. Look at the chart. Listen and write the name of the correct subway system.

1. Which subway system is the oldest? **2.** Which subway system is the cheapest for riders? **3.** Which subway system opened earlier—New York or Moscow? **4.** Which subway system has the fewest stations? **5.** Which subway system has more lines—London or Moscow? **6.** Which subway system transports the most passengers per day? **7.** Which subway system stays open the latest? **8.** Which subway system closes earlier—London or Moscow?

Page 66–Track 33

9. Fun facts. Listen and complete the sentences.

1. France has won the most gold medals for cycling. **2.** Italians drink the most bottles of bottled water. **3.** Walking is the most popular form of exercise in the United States. **4.** Americans are the greatest consumers of soda. **5.** *Spider Man* is one of the most expensive movies ever made. **6.** India produces more movies than any other country. **7.** Harvard University is the oldest university in the United States. **8.** The Chicago Public Library is one of the largest libraries in the United States.

Unit 12: Working Parents

Page 72–Track 34

9. Listen to these sentences. Circle the action that happens first.

1. He reads the newspaper before he eats breakfast.
2. She eats lunch after she washes her hands.
3. Before I get dressed, I listen to the weather report. **4.** She takes a walk before she eats dinner.
5. He always has a cup of coffee after he eats breakfast. **6.** As soon as I get to work, I call my husband. **7.** I watch TV after I do my homework.

Page 72–Track 35

10. Listen to these young people describe their families' expectations. Then, circle the correct verb in each sentence.

1. My mother doesn't let me dye my hair. **2.** In my country, girls can't go out on dates alone. **3.** Only my mother and father can drive the family car. **4.** My younger brothers are allowed to use the Internet when my parents are home. **5.** Children have to walk to school in groups. **6.** My sister can not talk on the phone at night. **7.** Children should help their parents at home. **8.** My friends can go to the movies at night, but my parents make me stay home.

Page 72–Track 36

11. Listen to Ella talk about her morning routine. Then, answer the questions.

I'm a working mother and morning is the busiest time of the day for me. I get up at 6:30 in the morning and the first thing I do is make my lunch. After that, I take a shower and get dressed. Then, I eat a small breakfast. I'm ready to wake up my son, Jesse, at about 7:15. Jesse is six months old. He wants a bottle as soon as he gets up. Then, I give him his breakfast. After breakfast, I change his diaper and get him dressed. He's very happy in the morning, and I have time to play and talk with him for about 20 minutes. At 8:15, I put him in his car seat and drive him to my mother's house. I'm really lucky because my mom only lives about two miles from me. She doesn't drive, so I drive to her house. She knows I love a cup of coffee in the morning, so she always has a fresh pot of coffee for me. We sit and talk for about 10 minutes. Then, it's time for me to leave for work.

Unit 13: Crime

Page 78–Track 37

7. Dictation. Listen and complete the sentences.

1. I was walking down the street when I saw a traffic accident. **2.** A man was driving into the intersection when a truck cut him off. **3.** The man in the car was beeping his horn when the truck driver suddenly stopped. **4.** After the truck stopped, both drivers got out of their vehicles. **5.** While they were arguing a taxi suddenly hit the back of the car. **6.** The taxi driver wasn't paying attention when he hit the car.
7. Fortunately, a police officer was coming out of a coffee shop when the accident happened.

Page 78–Track 38

8. Listen to the 911 phone call. Complete the summary of the phone call with appropriate words. You will have to listen to the conversation more than once.

Operator: 911. What's your emergency?
Cecilia: Hello. I think someone is in my house!
Operator: Are you in the house now?
Cecilia: No, I was coming home from work. I was pulling into my driveway when I noticed that the front door was open.
Operator: Was the door damaged?
Cecilia: I don't think so. In fact, I think the lights were on when I parked the car.
Operator: Where are you calling from?
Cecilia: I'm calling on a cell phone from my car in my driveway. Can you send an officer right away? I'm afraid to go into the house!
Operator: Of course. What's your name?
Cecilia: My name's Cecilia Roberts. I live at . . . Oh. Wait a minute! Someone's coming out of the house! Send someone quick!
Operator: I need your address, Cecilia.
Cecilia: It's 56 . . . wait a minute. It's my mother. She's taking my dog for a walk. There's no problem. I'm sorry.
Operator: That's alright, Cecilia. It happens all the time.

Unit 14: Careers

Page 84–Track 39

8. Listen to Mr. Miller's job interview. Then, read the questions and circle the answers.

W: So, tell me about yourself, Mr. Miller.
M: As you can see from my résumé, I graduated from college with a degree in computer programming.
W: Yes, I see. You worked for Tech Exec for two years. Is that right?
M: Yes, I was working as a programmer until two months ago. I was laid off. Twenty other programmers were laid off, too.
W: So, why are you applying for a sales position here at Family Computers?
M: First of all, I know computers. Second, I need a job and I hear that the benefits are very good. Also, there aren't many programming jobs right now.
W: That's right. The economy is slow, but our stores are doing well.
M: They are?
W: Yes. Let me tell you a little about the job. Our sales associates start at about $15 an hour. If you make a sale, you'll receive a 5% commission.
M: That's good.
W: Right. If your sales are good, after six months you'll receive a three-dollar-an-hour increase.

M: That's good to hear.
W: So, do you have any other work experience in the computer field?
M: Yes, I do. I used to volunteer at a youth center. I taught computer classes to teenagers. I enjoyed doing that.
W: Oh, really? We offer free computer classes on Saturdays. Would you be interested in teaching senior citizens?
M: Yes, I would.
W: Well, our time's up. Thank you for coming, Mr. Miller. If we're interested, you'll get a phone call this week.
M: Thank you for your time.

Page 84–Track 40

9. Listen and circle each correct main clause.

1. As soon as I closed the door, **2.** When she receives her check, **3.** If Charles gets home early, **4.** When the interview is over, **5.** Before Julia started work, **6.** If Matthew doesn't feel well,

Unit 15: City Life

Page 89–Track 41

5. Listen and circle the correct answers about the picture on page 88.

1. Has Elena been sitting in the park for an hour? **2.** Did she see the accident? **3.** Is she watching the wedding? **4.** Has Mark been working all morning? **5.** Does he work at the coffee shop full-time? **6.** Has Joseph been looking at Jane? **7.** Does Joseph want to talk to Jane? **8.** Is Officer Ortiz going to write an accident report? **9.** Did Mr. Thomas cause the accident? **10.** Is Mr. Thomas going to lose his job as a driver?

Page 90–Track 42

6. Listen and circle the sentence with the same meaning.

1. Emma was a waitress from 2000 to 2002. **2.** Larry began to work at 8:00. It's 1:00 now and he is still working. **3.** Gloria got to the train station an hour ago. Her train was supposed to come at 7:00, but it's not here yet. **4.** Every day Carla jogs in the park for 30 minutes before she goes to work. Carla is at work now. **5.** Thomas is in the clothing store looking at suits. At this moment he's trying on a blue suit. **6.** Bob is a hairstylist. It's 4:00 and he's very tired. He still has three more appointments today. **7.** Tuan retired in 2003 after working for the post office for 25 years. **8.** Lin turned on her computer six hours ago. She's still sitting at her desk.

Page 90

7. Listen to the conversations. Circle *T* for *True* or *F* for *False*.

Conversation 1–Track 43
A: Hi, George. How's everything?
B: Not too good. I'm still looking for a job.
A: They're looking for taxi drivers at my company. Why don't you apply?
B: Maybe I will.

Conversation 2–Track 44
A: Kathy, this is Bill. I'm stuck in traffic.
B: What time do you think you'll arrive? Your first patient is here.
A: I'm only about ten minutes away, but traffic is moving slowly.
B: I'll tell the patient that you'll be a little late.

Conversation 3–Track 45
A: How's Paul?
B: Paul? I'm not going out with Paul anymore. I'm dating a new guy, Joseph. He's wonderful. I'm going to introduce him to my parents soon.
A: Where did you meet him?
B: He lives in the apartment above me. Last month, I went upstairs and complained about the music in his apartment. He was having a party and he invited me to come in and enjoy the party.